The 81ˢᵗ Annual

WRITER'S DIGEST
WRITING COMPETITION
COLLECTION

THE GRAND PRIZE AND
FIRST-PLACE MANUSCRIPTS IN
EACH CATEGORY OF THE 81ˢᵀ ANNUAL
WRITER'S DIGEST WRITING COMPETITION

WRITER'S DIGEST
10151 Carver Road, Suite 200,
Blue Ash, OH 45242

These are works of fiction and nonfiction. As applicable, the events and characters described here are imaginary and are not intended to refer to specific places or living persons. The opinions expressed in these manuscripts are solely the opinions of the authors and do not represent the opinions or thoughts of the publisher or *Writer's Digest.*

CONTENTS

INTRODUCTION

The editors of Writer's Digest are pleased to share with you the winning entries in each category of the 81st Annual Writer's Digest Writing Competition, along with the Grand Prize-winning story, *A Marriage of Inconvenience*, by Jacob M. Appel.

A special thanks goes to our esteemed panel of judges:

CHILDREN'S/ YOUNG ADULT FICTION

HOLLY M. ALDER has taught writing since 1973. She directed the writing certification program at Principia College, taught writing classes for the University of Cincinnati and for their Upward Bound program, and currently teaches online writing classes for Writer's Digest University. She has degrees in English, Education, and Psychology; won a National Society of Arts and Letters honor award for her first play; and reads and collects children's books—over 6000.

GENRE SHORT STORY

MICHAEL J. VAUGHN is the author of thirteen novels, including "The Popcorn Girl," recently released on Amazon Kindle. His short stories and poetry have appeared in Many Mountains Moving, The Montserrat Review, and Terrain (forthcoming in Confrontation and The Blue Collar Review). He lives in San Jose, California, and has contributed two dozen articles to Writer's Digest.

INSPIRATIONAL WRITING

ANN BYLE is a freelance journalist for Publishers Weekly and Today's Christian Woman, and author of "The Making of a Christian Bestseller." She is also a literary agent and cofounder of Breathe Christian Writers Conference.

MAGAZINE FEATURE ARTICLE

SUSAN REYNOLDS began her thirty-year career as a journalist and a magazine editor. More recently, she has authored or edited more than twenty-five nonfiction and fiction books. Recently, she co-authored *Train*

Your Brain to Get Happy, Train Your Brain to Get Rich, Meditation for Moms, and *Healthiest You Ever.* Ms. Reynolds was the creator and editor of Adams Media's *My Hero* anthology series (four volumes) and *Woodstock Revisited, 50 far out, groovy, peace-inducing, flashback-inducing stories from those who were there.* Ms. Reynolds founded Literary Cottage, through which she offers writing, editing, and coaching services. Ms. Reynolds currently writes two blogs for Psychologytoday.com and has recently completed a memoir about the year she lived in Paris.

MAINSTREAM/ LITERARY SHORT STORY

DEBBY MAYNE is the author of more than 30 novels and novellas. *Waiting for a View* (July 2012) from B&H Publishing is the launch book in the quirky Bloomfield series written by eight authors. Also coming soon is her Class Reunion series with *Pretty Is as Pretty Does* (June 2013), *Bless Her Heart* (August 2013), and *Tickled Pink* (September 2013) from Abingdon Press. Debby and her husband Wally have two adult daughters, two sons-in-law, and two granddaughters.

MEMOIRS/PERSONAL ESSAY

HOLLIS GILLESPIE is an award-winning humor and travel columnist, with her column appearing every month on Atlanta magazine's coveted back page. She is also a best-selling memoirist, NPR commentator, professional speaker, comedian and guest on the Tonight Show with Jay Leno. She has been featured on scores of TV shows and blogs and runs Shocking Real Life, the largest writing school in Atlanta, which offers workshops on blogging and social media. Two of her books have been optioned for television. These days she gets most of her exercise running to catch flights. Contact Hollis through www.ShockingRealLife.com.

NON-RHYMING POETRY

KELLI RUSSELL AGODON is the author of *Letters from the Emily Dickinson Room* (White Pine Press, 2010), Winner of the ForeWord Magazine Book of the Year Prize in Poetry and a Finalist for the Washington State Book Award. She is also the author of *Small Knots* and the chapbook, *Ge-*

ography. Recently she co-edited the first eBook anthology of contemporary women's poetry, *Fire On Her Tongue*. Kelli is the editor of Seattle's literaryjournal, *Crab Creek Review* and the co-founder of Two Sylvias Press. She lives in the Northwest where she is a mountain biker and kayaker. She is currently at work on her third book of poems. Visit her at www. agodon.comor on her blog, Book of Kells at: www.ofkells.blogspot.com.

RHYMING POETRY

NANCY SUSANNA BREEN is a poet, freelance writer, and editor. Her poetry is available in e-chapbook form at Smashwords.com as is an e-book of writing prompts, *Nudged by Quotes—20 Writing Prompts Inspired by The World's Great Poetry, Volume 10: Poetical Quotations*. She's the former editor of *Poet's Market* and judges poetry contests at the state and national levels. Nancy blogs at Nudged2Write.com.

STAGE PLAY

JOE STOLLENWERK is the author of Today in History: Musicals and is currently pursuing his PhD in Theatre and Drama at Indiana University, where he also teaches Script Analysis. His adaptation of Margaret Atwood's The Handmaid's Tale premiered in CIncinnati in 2011 to wide acclaim.

TELEVISION/MOVIE SCRIPT

JESSICA DERCKS received her degree in theater from the California Institute of the Arts, and has worked on script development and production on such films as *Growth*, *Hold On Loosely* and *Look At Me*. Dercks began in story development, continuity and production, and has since taken that knowledge and experience and transferred it to script development and consultation. Over the years she has worked closely with writers, directors and producers to help improve their scripts and get their projects up and running.

Finally, our most heartfelt congratulations to the winners and the nearly 10,000 entries in this year's competition. The quality of your entries makes the judging more difficult each year. We look forward to seeing your work in the 81st Annual *Writer's Digest* Writing Competition Collection.

A MARRIAGE OF INCONVENIENCE

JACOB M. APPEL

CAST: 3 FEMALE / 2 MALE / 1 EITHER (OPTIONAL)

1 SET

Ninety year old Agatha Wellington, a wealthy widow, doubts the romantic virtues of men and desperately wants her granddaughter, Molly Drake, to marry a woman. Unfortunately for Agatha, Molly has fallen in love with a male art historian, Luther, who studies the written descriptions of lost surrealist paintings. Agatha is determined to foil this relationship—so determined that she consults a lawyer about having her property set on fire upon her death. As she explains to her attorney: "If my own granddaughter can't do me this one small favor, she doesn't see a dime." Without Agatha's knowledge, the lawyer then hires a female prostitute, Samantha, to seduce Molly. Meanwhile, Agatha demands that her granddaughter choose between her heterosexuality and her inheritance.

Zachariah, the lawyer, has a problem of his own. He is terrified of dying in his sleep, so much so that he suffers from debilitating insomnia. The tragedy of life, according to Zachariah, is that "even very wealthy people wake up dead." He consults his psychiatrist—who happens to be Molly Drake. When Agatha's granddaughter proves unable to cure him, he seeks help from the prostitute, whose motto is: "After sex with Samantha, you're ready to die." She cures him *too* well. He loses his fear of death entirely and begins to take unnecessary and "un-lawyerly" risks.

Agatha's threat to burn her fortune yields unexpected results: It turns out that included in the property she threatens to destroy is the "lost" painting to which Luther has dedicated years of study. The art historian finds himself facing a choice between the painting and his love for Agatha's granddaughter. His difficulties increase further when—with the help of a lightning strike—the prostitute does manage to seduce Molly. All appears lost for Luther...until Agatha meets Samantha and realizes that the prostitute is not the "decent young woman" she has had in mind for her granddaughter.

A Marriage of Inconvenience is a comedy of ideas that grapples with the issues of sexual orientation and property rights. The play is designed to be off-beat, provocative and fun.

CAST

2 MALE / 3 FEMALE / (1 EITHER)

Agatha Wellington	A wealthy widow of ninety years. **(F/90)**
Dr. Molly Drake	Agatha's granddaughter, a psychiatrist in her thirties. **(F/30s)**
Zachariah Carmichael	Agatha's attorney. **(M/40s-50s)**
Luther Gibbons	Heir to a board game fortune. **(M/30s)**
Samantha	An entrepreneurial prostitute. It would help if she had a foreign accent. **(F/20s-30s)**
An Authoritative Voice	The **Voice** may be played by one actor. Alternatively, each of the five actors may take a turn playing the **Voice** for those scenes in which he or she does not otherwise appear.

SET & PROPS

The set should be as sparse as possible. Every scene in the play can be staged with a door, a small table or desk, a telephone, a chess set, and either three chairs, two chairs, one chair, or no chairs; several scenes in Act

Two also require a bed. The only other prop is Bergault's surrealist painting: *The Resurrection of Dismas and Gestas.* The audience should never see the painted side of the canvas.

NOTE ON SUBTITLES

The bold headings preceding each scene (eg. "**Agatha**"; "**Zachariah visits his psychiatrist**") should be read aloud by the **Voice**, preferably over a microphone.

ACT ONE

1. "Agatha"

       (Agatha enters. Agatha, to the audience.)

      AGATHA
I am ninety years old.

Happy birthday to me.

You are wondering: Am I a young ninety or an old ninety?

Only young people wonder: Are you a young ninety or an old ninety?

You can be a young seventy-five. You can be an old seventy-five.

You *cannot* be a young ninety.

People ask me: What is your secret?

I tell them. A woman needs three qualities to live to be ninety.

Quality number one. Ignorance.

That gets you through the first thirty years.

Quality number two. Flattery.

That's another three decades.

Quality number three. Spite.

Years sixty through ninety.

After that, I don't know yet.

2. "Zachariah"
(Zachariah enters. Zachariah, to the audience.)

ZACHARIAH
I'm having difficulty sleeping.

I'm afraid that I might wake up dead.

That is the great irony of life: A man graduates first in his class at the Yale Law School and he *still* might wake up dead.

My work offers little comfort.

I am a wills and trusts attorney. I manage the estates of very wealthy people. Even very wealthy people wake up dead.

Last spring, I attended my law school class reunion. Twenty years. I ran into an old friend, a human rights activist named Jack Stone. He slapped me on the back and asked: "Wills and estates? Profiteering off rich, dead people? How do you sleep at night?"

Jack Stone was in the newspaper yesterday. He woke up dead.

3. "Agatha visits her lawyer"
(Zachariah sits down at his desk. Agatha sits opposite him.)

AGATHA
So I wish to rewrite my will. Change the beneficiary.

ZACHARIAH
All right, Mrs. Wellington. We can do that.

AGATHA
How quickly?

ZACHARIAH
Very quickly.

AGATHA

At my age, you understand, every waking moment counts.

ZACHARIAH

I understand.....Who would you like to be the new beneficiary?

AGATHA

Me.

ZACHARIAH

You?

AGATHA

Me. I desire to be buried with my property. Like the ancient Egyptians.

ZACHARIAH

I see, Mrs. Wellington. What about your granddaughter?

AGATHA

Why for heaven's sake would I want to be buried with her?

ZACHARIAH

What I meant, Mrs. Wellington, was that you're disinheriting your granddaughter.

AGATHA

Exactly. And why shouldn't I? She's been going on dates behind my back. *With men.*

ZACHARIAH

I don't know that it's any of my business, but your granddaughter must be what? Thirty years old?

AGATHA

Thirty-two. An old maid.

ZACHARIAH

Don't you think thirty-two is old enough to go on dates?

AGATHA

To go on dates? Most certainly. But not with *men*. I did not raise my granddaughter to date *men*. It's nothing personal, you understand. Some of my closest friends are *men*. Molly's grandfather was a *man*. But *Molly* is going to marry a woman....I'm a grown adult too, Mr. Carmichael, and if my own granddaughter can't do me this one small favor, she doesn't see a dime.

ZACHARIAH
All right, Mrs. Wellington. I'll look into what can be done—but I'm afraid this isn't the easiest matter....Some things are not possible....

AGATHA
What do you mean: "Some things are not possible"? You're a lawyer. Make it possible.
(Agatha exits.)

4. Molly
(Molly enters. Molly, to the audience.)

MOLLY
They say a woman over thirty with a doctorate has a higher chance of being struck by lightning than of getting married.

I have *two* doctoral degrees. One in thanatology. One in medicine.

This was not wise romantic strategy.

I am a psychiatrist. I spend all of my time at the hospital.

This is also not wise romantic strategy.

The only people I speak to all day are doctors and patients. I speak to nurses too—but they are like doctors, only not doctors.

I would not want to marry a doctor.

Psychiatrists are not permitted to marry their patients. The rules are very strict about this. They do not make any exceptions—even if the psychiatrist and the patient are in love.

I think they should make an exception if the psychiatrist and the patient are in love.

5. "Zachariah visits his psychiatrist"
   (Molly sits down in a chair. Zachariah enters and sits opposite her.)

ZACHARIAH
I don't think I'm overreacting, Dr. Drake. I think everyone else is *under*-reacting.

MOLLY
How so?

ZACHARIAH
Most people don't think about waking up dead.

MOLLY
And you do.

ZACHARIAH
People are so vulnerable when they're sleeping. But they don't realize it. They just lie there counting sheep. I lie there and think about what would happen if the couple in the apartment below mine left their gas range on by mistake....

MOLLY
What *would* happen?

ZACHARIAH
They say carbon monoxide poisoning is quick and painless. You don't even know you're dying—you think you have the flu. I can imagine only one thing worse than dying: Dying without knowing that you're dying.

MOLLY
Have you considered sleeping with a window open?

ZACHARIAH
I tried that. I lay there all night worrying that a prowler might climb through the window and strangle me.

(Zachariah exits.)

6. "Luther"

(Luther enters. Luther, to the audience.)

LUTHER

My father designs and manufactures board games.

My father is a very powerful board game magnate. I am heir to a board game empire.

Board games are not like real life.

In *Monopoly*, everyone begins with the same amount of money. In real life, everyone *does not* begin with the same amount of money. My father does not believe all people should begin life with the same amount of money. That is the one matter on which most people agree. Democrats and Republicans. Jews and Christians. There is a consensus that some people should begin life with more money than others.

I *do not* manufacture board games. I am an art historian. I study the paintings of the eighteenth century French surrealist Renée Bergault.

I imagine you have never heard of Bergault. His workshop burned during the French Revolution and none of the canvasses survived. All that remains are written descriptions of his paintings.

They are quite beautiful.

7. "Molly"

(Molly, to the audience.)

MOLLY

People *do* get struck by lightning.

Some people get struck by lightning *more than once.*

I read about a woman in Georgia who was struck by a lightning sixteen times.

And she didn't even have a Ph. D....

Scientists now know that some people are lightning magnets. They are far more likely to be struck by lightning than anybody else. If lightning strikes were distributed randomly, the odds of any one person being struck by lightning sixteen times would be one trillion-billion to one. But lightning strikes are not distributed randomly.

Scientists cannot explain why some people attract lightning.

I think about this a lot.

It is the sort of thing you think about when you are not in love.

8. "Molly goes on a date"
(Luther sits down at a table. Molly sits opposite him.)

LUTHER
I've been thinking a lot about walking on water.
It seems obvious to you and to me that we can't walk on water. That's why Jesus is such a big deal. But if you were a Martian who'd arrived on earth for the first time, you wouldn't know that you couldn't walk on water. Just by looking at the water, you can't tell that you can't walk on it. You'd probably see all those boats on the river and you'd assume you *could* walk on water.

MOLLY
This is the strangest date I've ever been on.

LUTHER
Strange in a good way or strange in a bad way?

MOLLY
Strange in a *strange* way....But good, I think....
May I ask you a very odd question?

LUTHER
Anything.

MOLLY

Are you ever afraid of waking up dead?

LUTHER
What?

MOLLY
I have this patient, a middle-aged lawyer, who's afraid he'll die in his sleep. I assured him his fears are irrational—but I've hardly slept for three days since.

LUTHER
Because you're afraid?

MOLLY
Aren't you?

LUTHER
That raises an interesting theological question. If true Christians believe that the afterlife is preferable to this one, why don't they hold murderers in higher esteem?

MOLLY
Excuse me?

LUTHER
I'm sorry. I know one is not supposed to discuss religion on a first date.

MOLLY
Is this only our *first* date?

LUTHER
I've never understood *why* one isn't supposed to discussion spiritual matters on a first date. Do you believe in the afterlife? I ask that only because there are people all over this country who've been married for years and they don't know whether their spouses believe in the afterlife.

MOLLY
Is that a proposal?

LUTHER

May I ask you a very odd question?

MOLLY
Anything.

LUTHER
Do you ever wonder if Martians can swim?
(Molly and Luther exit.)

9. "Agatha"
(Agatha enters. Agatha, to the audience.)

AGATHA
If I were a Native American and I wanted my granddaughter to find a husband who shared our heritage, few people would object.

If I were Jewish and I wanted my granddaughter to marry a Jewish person, that would be perfectly acceptable.

Well I'm female, so I'd like my granddaughter to find a nice young woman. Maybe a librarian or a dental hygienist. I don't understand what the big fuss is.

10. "Zachariah visits his client"
(Agatha opens the door. Zachariah enters.)

ZACHARIAH
It can't be done, Mrs. Wellington.

AGATHA
What's that?

ZACHARIAH
You can't bury yourself with your belongings.

AGATHA
Why in heaven's name not? They're *my* belongings, aren't they?

ZACHARIAH

You have to be mentally competent to execute a will in this state, Mrs. Wellington. I've spoken with three experts on inheritance law and *all three* agree that expressing a wish to be buried alongside your property would be *prima facie* evidence that you are *not* mentally competent.

AGATHA

Then find another expert, Mr. Carmichael. That's the one thing we'll never run out of in this country: Experts. Sometimes it amazes me how we can live in a nation with so many experts and so little expertise.

ZACHARIAH

It doesn't work like that, Mrs. Wellington....I think it might be productive for us to explore other options. If you don't want to leave your money to your granddaughter, how about to a favorite charity?

AGATHA

I don't have a favorite charity. I don't care for charities. These days, everybody wants to fix something or save something or cure something. Cancer. Hemorrhoids. Well when I was a girl, we hadn't fixed or cured half of these things. And do you know what? People were happier.

ZACHARIAH

And you have no other relatives? Maybe a close friend?

AGATHA

I'm ninety years old, Mr. Carmichael. Everybody I've ever known is dead.

ZACHARIAH

Then I'm not sure what to tell you, Mrs. Wellington. I can't write you a defective will.

AGATHA

What happens if I leave a will without any beneficiary?

ZACHARIAH

Your next-of-kin inherits. In your case, that would be your granddaughter.

AGATHA
And if I add a clause specifically disinheriting her?

ZACHARIAH
Then the property *escheats* to the state.

AGATHA
Escheats?

ZACHARIAH
The state takes everything.

AGATHA
That's mighty convenient for the state, isn't it?

ZACHARIAH
It rarely comes to that.

AGATHA
Well there won't be any *escheating* when I'm gone. I don't even like the state....Do *you* like the state, Mr. Carmichael?

ZACHARIAH
I'm not sure what you mean. Do you mean *this* state? Or the concept of "the state"?

AGATHA
Never mind.

ZACHARIAH
I have an idea, Mrs. Wellington. Maybe you could spend all of your money before you die.

AGATHA
Now *that* is a truly asinine suggestion. You are either over-estimating my time or underestimating my wealth. Do you know how much I'm worth, Mr. Carmichael?

ZACHARIAH

Yes, I do.

AGATHA

Well, I don't. This is what happens when you're married to a *man*. He earns a vast fortune and then he dies and then you're stuck all alone with a vast fortune. I read in the newspaper that I was worth somewhere between six hundred million and eight hundred million dollars. When you read that about a *man*, you think: Good God! That's an awful lot of money. When you read that about a woman, you think: Between six hundred million and eight hundred million. How can she not know how much money she has?

ZACHARIAH

I imagine it would be difficult to spend eight hundred million dollars in a short period of time. Or even six hundred million.

AGATHA

And what if I miscalculated and spent too much? I'd die in a debtors prison.

ZACHARIAH

I see your point, Mrs. Wellington—though, for the record, there aren't debtors prisons anymore.

AGATHA

Not at the moment. But they'll come back. That's the one thing you realize when you've lived ninety years. *Everything* comes back....swing music, Richard Nixon, the ivory-billed woodpecker. Also witch hunts, concentration camps, torture chambers. Everything. Only the victims are sometimes different. Do you know what, Mr. Carmichael?

ZACHARIAH

No, Mrs. Wellington. What?

AGATHA

Next time around, I think we should have *creditors* prisons.

ZACHARIAH

Please, Mrs. Wellington. With regard to the matter at hand—

AGATHA

Any more asinine ideas?

ZACHARIAH

Maybe you could arrange to be sued, Mrs. Wellington. Let someone take you for all you're worth.

AGATHA

And die poor? No, indeed....If the United States is such a communist country that I cannot be buried with my own property, then nobody may have it. I would prefer it be destroyed upon my death. Set on fire. Like one of those Indian widows.

ZACHARIAH

You want me to write *that* into your will?

A UNICORN'S HORN TASTES LIKE VANILLA

BROOKE HARTMAN

Of all the beasties we dragons eat, the unicorn is the most scrumptious of them all. I would pluck them from the forests like popcorn, munch their marzipan flanks, crunch their caramel hooves, and slurp their raspberry filling off my claws. But I always saved the horn for last: the vanilla candy creampuff horn.

I gazed sadly upon my dinner: a troll caught stealing my gold. Trolls are the worst. Their skin is as brittle as bark, their toes are tough as toadstools, and they're as slimy as a snail.

I lifted the squealing troll to my jaws and silenced it with a crunch.

How I longed for a unicorn.

The bushes rustled and out trotted a cinnamon bun fawn.

Ahh, dessert! I curled up in my den, closed my eyes and pretended to sleep.

The fawn wandered right into my reach. With a flick of a claw, I lifted it, crying and wiggling, up to one of my eyes.

"Well, you're not a unicorn," I said. "But you'll do just fine."

"A unicorn?" asked the fawn. Its voice was sweet as pecan pie.

"Don't interrupt me while I'm eating," I said.

"I do apologize," said the fawn, "but did you say you wanted a unicorn?"

"So what if I did?" I replied.

"Because, sir," said the fawn. "I know where you can find one."

I laughed, and the fawn cringed. Dragons are not known for their oral hygiene.

"I haven't laid teeth on a unicorn in hundreds of years," I said. "There aren't any left. They've all been eaten by dragons like me."

"That's not true!" cried the fawn. "There are entire herds of them if you just know where to look."

"Entire herds, you say?" I said, releasing it from my claws. "You will show me where these unicorns are. But if you're lying to me"—I snapped my jaws within inches of the fawn's head— "You're as good as fawn figgy pudding, understand?"

"Yes, sir," replied the fawn. "But it's very far away. It would be much quicker to fly."

"Very well," I said. "But if I fly, then you are going with me!"

Before the fawn could turn its tootsie roll tail and run, I snatched it up and began to beat my wings in wide strokes.

"Which way?" I demanded.

The fawn pointed north.

The wind filled my wings as we glided over fields of tempting delights: Spun sugar sheep. Butter brickle buffaloes. Chocolate moose. I licked my lips and thought about stopping for an in flight snack. But there were unicorns ahead. *Unicorns!* I could almost feel their custard cream bodies between my teeth.

The air grew colder and the ground beneath us became frosted with snow.

"There!" the fawn cried.

Before us lay the great northern sea.

I landed on the frozen shore and stared out at the waves.

"Where are they?" I roared. "I want a unicorn NOW!"

Then the waves broke and an entire candy shop of vanilla creamsicle horns surfaced on the sea. Drool dripped from my jaws as I watched the waves wash over their frosting flanks.

I longed to dive into those chilly waves after them. But despite the fairy stories you may have heard, a dragon cannot swim. Our bodies are mighty with muscle. Our wings are broad as a ship's sails. Our claws are big as clubs and sharp as daggers. But there is not one bit of a dragon that can float.

"When will they come out of the water?" I asked the fawn.

But there was no answer. The fawn had wriggled from my grasp. Its root beer rump was already a speck on the southern horizon. But what did a crumb of fawn matter now that there were unicorns? Sweet, scrumptious unicorns?

So I gazed upon the sea, watching the unicorns nuzzle the air, and waited.

I waited until the sun sizzled like cinnamon on the horizon.

I waited through the night, filled with lights of lime and grape and lemon.

I waited until the sun popped into the sky like a buttered pancake.

Then I was done waiting.

In a hurricane of snowflakes, I spread my wings and glided over the waves until I was over the unicorns. I slashed my claws at them, roaring mightily. But they quickly sank out of reach. I hovered there as long as I could, but soon I grew tired and had to return to shore.

Frustration made me hungry. I poked around on the beach and found some chocolate bon bon things with fat whiskered faces and spun sugar tusks. They made a horrible *ork! ork!* sound and left a rubbery taste in my mouth. So I only ate about twenty of them.

By then, the unicorns had returned. I gazed at them, feeling sad and hopeless.

For days, I watched their meringue muzzles bob among the waves, and with each day my longing for them grew.

Then, one day, some new creatures came wandering by. They were a strange bunch, toddling on two legs and wrapped in furs with just their round faces poking out. As soon as they caught sight of me, they began hollering in gibberish and poking their toothpicks in my direction.

So I ate them.

All but one, that is. I snatched it up and dangled it in front of my face.

"You!" I said, blasting it with smoke. "Tell me how to get a unicorn!"

But all it said was, "Aaaaaagh!"

So I ate that one too.

For a long while after that, no other creatures came. The bon bon things had vanished (though that may have been because I ate them all) and I had not seen another two legged creature since the group of them met its fate in my jaws.

Each day, the sun rose lower in the sky. Then one morning it did not rise at all.

The air was so cold my flames turned to ash and my scales grew thick with ice.

My sadness grew so strong that I—a dragon!—did an unspeakable thing. I began to cry. Because what I really wanted more than anything was a lip smacking, claw licking, custard cream bite of unicorn. And there they were, just beyond my reach, splashing among the cold, dark waves.

That was when I heard the laughter. I puffed out my chest and forced a trickle of smoke from my nostrils, prepared to show whoever it was why no one *ever* laughs at a dragon. Then I saw it: a marshmallow bear, giggling and pointing his paws in my direction.

"Are you the one waiting for the unicorns?" the bear snickered.

"What do you know about it?" I asked.

But the bear just kept laughing.

With a swipe of my claws, I pinned the bear to the ice, about to take a bite from its buttery behind.

"Wait!" cried the bear. "Let me go, and I'll get you a unicorn!"

Fixing it with a menacing stare, I loosened my claws. The bear wiggled from my grasp and slipped its whipped cream body into the sea. Soon there was a great splashing and clashing that brought a flutter of hope to my heart. The bear turned back, clutching something custard soft in its jaws. At last the bear reached the shore and tossed the thing at my feet.

"Here's your unicorn," it said with a smirk.

I stared in disgust at the jiggly, jelly lump. "What *is* it?"

"It's a narwhale, you silly dragon!" said the bear, hooting with laughter.

"A *narwhale*?" I roared. The coals in my belly began to ignite. Smoke billowed from my jaws as I snapped them together with a thunderous gnash of teeth.

The bear stopped laughing. Its black licorice eyes grew wide. Then it turned and started to run. With a roaring whoosh, a streak of fire shot from my lungs, sending the bear yelping and howling and scooting his flaming behind against the snow.

"Don't go far," I called. "I love toasted marshmallows!"

I turned back to the narwhale, now frozen against the ice. With a flick of a claw, I pried it from the ground and swallowed it whole. It was a bit chewy, but it did have a pleasant strawberry texture. And was it my imagination, or did the horn taste just a little bit like vanilla?

I considered hunting the bear down and making it fetch me another narwhale. But it was time I got back to my forest. With one last glance toward the sea, I shook the ice from my wings and lifted from the snow, heading south.

At last I reached my forest. I had just curled up in my den when I heard a rustling in the bushes. I opened one eye in time to see a mighty brown sugar stag emerge from the woods, crowned with a pair of candied chestnut antlers.

Ahh, dessert! I narrowed my eyes and pretended to sleep.

The stag approached me with its head held high. "You can't fool me, dragon," it said.

At once, I recognized it as the fawn. "You!" I cried.

"Did you ever get yourself a unicorn?" it asked. "Or should I say… narwhale?"

"You knew?" I bellowed, puffing smoke and flames. "You led me to that frozen wasteland and you *knew*?"

"I hoped you would stay in that wasteland and stop pestering this forest for good," said the stag. "But here you are, back from your journey, with new morsels in your greedy belly."

I spat out a little flame of anger. But deep inside, I knew the stag was right—though I was a dragon, and so, of course, would never admit it.

"Rest now, dragon," said the stag, turning back toward the forest. "But when you've had your rest, perhaps you'd like to take another vacation?"

"Vacation?" I shouted. "You call freezing my tail off a vacation?"

But there was no reply. The stag was gone.

I crawled back into my den, thinking of what the stag had said.

It was true. I had grown tired of booger flavored trolls. The narwhale had actually been quite tasty. And I had heard rumors of lands with grape gumdrop gazelles, plum pudding pandas, and even horses made of white and dark chocolate.

Maybe I *would* take a vacation. I would sample all the cuisines of the world, from candy corn cockatiels to peppermint patty penguins. And there was always the chance that in my travels I would find a real lip smacking, claw licking, custard pie unicorn, with Hershey kissed hooves, and a red raspberry rump, and a creampuff horn that would crunch between my teeth and taste like vanilla.

MAKING GOOD NEIGHBORS

ANN M. SLIGAR

The calves were bunched up in the fence corner, bawling nervously as the three dogs circled back and forth in front of them. Any moment now one of them would panic and make a break, and the killing chase would be on. Sue Ann had had to put two claves down after the last attack and couldn't afford to lose any more. She took several deep breaths to clear her mind of the anger and frustration before sighting on the pack leader. She recognized it. It had led the attack on Jock. The other dogs didn't seem to notice when it collapsed. They were used to gun shots. When the second dog fell the third got the message and ran, but not far.

She hurried back to the barn for the tractor. As quickly as she could, she loaded the dogs into the tractor bucket. All three were scarred veterans of the Hoggesses' illegal Saturday night dog fights. She dumped the bodies behind the loafing shed in the big pasture, and dug a hole with the bucket. After burying the dogs, she used the bucket to scoop out the floor of the shed. Not how she'd planned to spend the morning. On the other hand cleaning out the shed was long overdue. At least now she could mark that off her growing list of deferred chores. The shed provided more than enough manure. The big smelly pile would hide the grave from varmints—and from the Hoggesses.

She had a clear legal right to shoot dogs that attacked livestock on her property, but the Hoggess family had little regard for laws. Jim Cordles, who had the farm across the road, had also lost calves to their dogs. He had killed two of the pack he caught attacking his cows. Two days later he found his fences cut, six cows dead, and several calves mutilated. After that he had just taken the losses. But he had a large herd. Sue Ann didn't. She couldn't afford to lose a single one of hers.

Sue Ann had never though she could hate another person, but she hated the Hoggesses. So did most of the neighbors and many of the townspeople, who usually referred to them simply as the Hogs. The Hogs were mean and destructive, and went out of their way to cause harm any way they could. On top of the livestock losses, she was facing a huge bill for her border collie Jock, who was still at the vet's, recuperating from a savage attack by the Hoggess dogs. Jock wasn't just her friend and companion, he was her right hand. She couldn't manage without him. One person cannot work cows by themselves. She had to have Jock's help. Occasionally she daydreamed about getting a second border collie, but well trained herders were just too expensive and she didn't have time to train a pup.

She checked on the calves. They had calmed down, and were grazing. None of them showed any signs of injury. Relieved, she hosed off the tractor and put it back in the shed; weeded the garden; collected eggs; and checked that the water tanks were full. By that time she was running a bit late. After a quick shower, she put on the blue dress that had been Tommy's favorite, and headed to the VA hospital. An IED had blown off half of Tommy's arm and sent a chunk of metal into his head. The doctors said his recovery was going well. The new prosthesis had given him back the missing hand, and his brain was functioning much better than they had expected. He'd never be back to what he had been before, but they thought he would be able to go home before too long. A lot of the men in his ward never would.

By the time she got home it was nearly dark. She checked on the livestock, but was too tired to eat. She undressed, leaving her good clothes in a pile on the floor, and crawled into bed. Her old cat Jimmy joined her. She curled around his welcome warmth and cried herself to sleep.

She was checking the fences when she found the deer carcass. It had been shot several times with a semi-automatic weapon. There had been no attempt to take any of the meat. The waste sickened her. Not far beyond its pathetic, crumped body she found a hole in the fence. The wires had been cut and tracks from a pair of four-wheelers. They had raced around the pasture, leaving a maze of ruts in the grass. The damage was extensive. The poet Robert Frost had been wrong when he wrote that *good fences make good neighbors*. Not if you lived next to the Hogs. Sue

Ann fought down tears, but couldn't stop her hands from shaking with the anger that threatened to overwhelm her. It took longer than it should have to repair the fence.

She returned to the house just as the Hog's pickup pulled up. She pulled the tractor up to the gate, blocking the drive. Hoggess got out, followed by his sons Dan and Zach, and one of the grandsons. They were an ill-favored lot, especially Dan. He had the rotten teeth and cadaverous look of a meth freak. Sue thought the grandson might be heading down the same road.

"We're looking for our dogs." Zach said. "You seen them?"

"No."

"We heard shots yesterday," Zach said. "Know anything about that?"

"I shot a possum that had gotten into the chicken house."

"Yeah? What'd you do with it?"

"Put it in the garbage." She pointed to the empty trash bin sitting by the road. The truck had been by less than an hour earlier. Some days you got lucky.

"What you need is a good dog," Zach said. "Keep them possums away." He gave her a malicious grin. They knew that their dogs had nearly killed Jock.

"We'll just take a look around." Hoggess said. "See if we can find the dogs. Could of come through the fence over to here. Need to move the tractor Missy."

"You're welcome to look around, but not in the truck."

"Why the hell not? You hiding something?" His habitual scowl deepened into an angry glare.

"The last two times you've driven in here you left the gates open and the cows got into the garden and the hayfield."

"You just think you're something, don't you?" Zach said. "Living in your big fancy house. Lording it over the rest of us." Sue looked over at the century-old house. Tommy's great-grandfather had built it. It was a simple four room farm house in serious need of paint and a new roof. Not even the wildest stretch of the imagination could consider it big or fancy. "You ain't nothing special, cunt. You and that stupid brain-dead shit of a husband of yours ain't nothing."

"Aw, come on Uncle Zack," the grandson said. He gave Sue Ann a grimace that was probably supposed to be a leer. "She's probably just on the rag. You know how uppity and bitchy women get then. Like you always say, she's just needing a good fuck to straighten her out."

What is it with men of this sort, Sue Ann wondered. So many of them seemed to think a quick roll in the hay, with them of course, is all that's required to make a woman all happy and compliant. Speaking of brain-dead. She felt sorry for their women. No wonder they'd all left. All except Dan's drug-addicted daughter Jane who was so far gone she couldn't function on her own.

"Get back in the truck," Hoggess said. "We're going. And you." He pointed a grimy finger in Sue Ann's face. "Don't think we won't find out if you done something to our dogs. You'll be real sorry if you did."

"Mr. Hoggess, I haven't seen your dogs." She let the tiredness sound in her voice. He gave her a long hard stare. She returned it unflinchingly. He turned on his heel and stalked to the truck. She heard Zack mutter "Stupid cunt. She ain't so great," as he climbed in the back.

The next morning was the worst she could remember. She moved the cows from the north pasture to the fifty-acre. Most of them went right in when she opened the gate, but a few had to be rounded up and driven in. It took her forever to get them all through the gate. She was nearly exhausted from running back and forth trying to make them go where she wanted. She really missed Jock. He'd have had them moved in no time.

She was checking for stragglers in the dip by the creek when she found what was left of Astro's Lady May. She'd been shot. Sue Ann had paid more than she could afford for her—Lady's outstanding bloodlines were going to improve the herd; attract new buyers; raise the price Sue Ann could ask for the calves. Part of one loin was cut out. With a chain-saw by the look of it. It had to have happened when she was at the VA. Too long now for her to call in the meat processer to salvage the rest of the carcass. That had been before they knew the dogs were missing. It wasn't retaliation. They had just wanted some steaks. It was pure damned bad luck it had been Lady May. At least she had the two calves. They were both heifers so it wasn't a complete loss.

As she closed the side gate she saw the Hoggess grandsons in the front yard. They sprinted for their four-wheelers when they saw her. They yelled insults she couldn't quite hear over the roar of the engines. One of them gave her the finger as they tore away. She started to run, but then slowed to a walk, dreading what she would find. It was even worse than she had expected. They had rammed through the fence, pushing over posts and breaking the pickets. Her flower garden was gone; the birdbath Tommy had given her for their anniversary smashed, and the plants ground into the dirt. They had spray painted the house with every dirty word they'd ever heard and a couple that they appeared to have made up.

Finding Jimmy was what finally broke her. Jimmy liked and trusted people. In all his years no one had ever mistreated him. He wouldn't have known he should run. She sat on the porch steps, rocking back and forth as she cradled his poor mutilated body. She howled her anguish to the sky until she was hoarse. She finally got up when there were no more tears. Her eyes were so swollen, she could barely see as she went in to find a box good enough for him. She wrapped him in the little rug he had loved to sleep on, and carefully tucked him into the box with his favorite toys. She buried him in the old family cemetery off by the little orchard. She sat and talked to him until well after dark.

She was halfway back to the house when it hit her. When Tommy came home he was bound to run into the Hogs. The horrible men who loved to torment Willie Causon who had downs syndrome; calling him stupid, retard, and dummy, and making crude jokes about him and about his frail, wheel-chair bound mother. What would they say to Tommy? Tommy, with his missing hand, awkward limp, and disfigured face. Tommy, who was still dealing with the horrors and brutality he had experienced. Tommy, who finally had his PTSD under control—a very fragile control.

Sue Ann put on her black jeans, a close fitting black turtleneck, and black fingerless gloves. She got the old sniper rifle Dad had brought back from Nam out of the gun safe and loaded it. It was in perfect working order, kept that way just as dad had shown her. Extra shells went into her belt pouch. When she reached the Hog's woods she pulled down the rolled up black ski mask. She positioned the rifle on top of the little hill overlooking the house.

The only light came from the open doors of the workshop and a house window, but the night scope gave her a clear view of the group at the picnic table. Hoggess sat facing his boys. The table top was littered with whiskey and beer bottles, and dirty plates. The grandsons were passing a joint back and forth as they leaned against a nearby stump. A radio in the shop was blasting away at top volume, filling the night with the tinny sound of blown speakers.

The first shot hit Hoggess dead center. The second one took out Zach. As he toppled off the bench the man next to him shot to his feet. It wasn't Dan. The nondescript little man was a complete stranger. He was holding a pistol. He looked around frantically then ducked low and started running a zigzag course toward the shop. She ignored him as she dropped first one then the other grandson. She found the man again as he dove through the shop door. Shouts erupted inside, followed by a fairly spectacular explosion.

Sue waited several minutes, but no one came out. She strolled down to the picnic table. The burning building provided plenty of light. A dull gleam caught her eye. The stranger's pistol was lying on the ground near the table. She picked it up. One of the grandsons was still moving. She shot him in the forehead then did the same for the other three Hogs. They might survive a body shot, but no one walked away from a 38 slug in the brain.

She eased up onto the house porch. The door was open. She stayed near the hallway wall to a avoid creaking boards as she cautiously made her way toward the living room. Jane was out cold on the sofa. The battered coffee table was covered with drug paraphernalia. Judging from what Sue Ann had seen on TV, Jane was now mainlining coke. She slipped into the room and froze. A sleepy toddler sat up in the recliner. She held her finger to her lips. He yawned, and snuggled down beside his sleeping sister. There was no one else in the house. She picked a discarded shirt off the floor. After wiping down the pistol, she wrapped it in the shirt, and pitched it into the blazing shop. The fire was so hot she had to stand back quite a way, but she was, after all, the ladies' softball star pitcher.

She retrieved Dad's rifle and went home. For the first time in ages she had no trouble falling asleep.

Sue Ann had secured new rails to the reset fence posts, and was screwing the unbroken pickets back on when Charley West's squad car coasted to a stop on the shoulder. She pulled a bandanna out of her hip pocket and wiped her face as he and a deputy got out.

"Morning, Charley."

"Morning Sue Ann. Looks like you had a little trouble." He tossed a stray piece onto the pile of broken pickets. His deputy grunted and stared around. He was new and had a reputation of still being a bit gung ho.

"Yeah. The Hog boys paid me a friendly visit yesterday."

"Humm. You hear any gunshots over that way last night?"

"Hell, Charley, I hear shots nearly every night. They're always shooting at something."

"Yeah. How about an explosion?" He held the piece of picket she was using as a spacer. "Screwing it back together, huh?"

"Yeah. They hold better than nails. An explosion? Over at Hoggesses? What time?" She kept the drill steady as she secured the picket.

"Round about midnight, best we can tell."

"Nah. I went to bed early. Tired out from scraping paint." She jerked her thumb toward the house. Despite her best efforts, a lot of the graffiti was still legible. "What exploded?"

"Meth lab. FBI's had their eye on the operation for a while. They've been selling to some big drug dealers. We were planning a raid, but someone beat us to the punch. Shot them all. Mail carrier found them this morning. There were two bodies in the lab. We're assuming one of them is Dan, but they were too badly burned to identify. We'll have to wait for the lab reports to find out who the other one was."

"All the Hoggesses?" It wasn't hard for Sue to look shocked. She hadn't thought about who might find them. She was sorry it was Mary. She'd recently lost her husband and didn't need to see a bunch of bodies. "Not Jane, too? What about the kids?"

"No, they're fine. Jane was so stoned she slept through it all."

"Who did it?"

"According to the little boy it was ninjas."

"Ninjas? Don't tell me the Japanese Yakuza is moving in on the Hog's operation. Did they carry Samurai swords?" Charley shared her grin.

"No. Just miscreants dressed in black with face masks, or maybe I should say *a* miscreant. The boy only saw one," the deputy said disapprovingly. He seemed to take it as a personal affront. "What about you? I heard you're good with a gun."

"Sue Ann was on the Olympic team, Dale," Charley said with the pride the locals all felt in her accomplishment.

"Well. It looks like she's got plenty of reason to want the Hoggesses out of the way."

"Yeah." Charley frowned at him and heaved a sigh. "Sorry, Sue Ann, but I've got to ask. You still got Tommy's sniper rifle?"

"No. Sold it to Martin last year to help pay for re-drilling the well."

"Who's Martin?" Dale asked suspiciously.

"Martin Delahardt. Owns the gun shop in town."

"Do you know if he's still got it?" Charley asked, heading Dale off.

"No idea. He did say he had a customer who was wanting one. Collector from out of town, I think."

"Thanks, Sue Ann. We'll check it out with Martin. Come on Dale." He turned back as Dale got in the car. "Should have asked earlier. How's Tommy doing?"

"Well, you had things on your mind. He's good. The docs say he may be able to come home soon."

"Glad to hear it."

"Say, Charley, does your wife still have those kittens?" She lowered her voice. "The Hoggess boys killed Jimmy and I need a cat around the place."

"I'm real sorry to hear that. He was a nice old cat. Some folks might say whoever shot the Hogs did us all a favor. I'll tell Stacy you'll be by for a kitten."

Two weeks later Sue Ann got a call from the VA. The doctors had decided Tommy was well enough to come home for the weekend. A test visit, they called it. If it went well, he might be able to come home permanently. Tommy was so happy to get home he cried. They spent the day wandering arm-in-arm over every inch of the place. She had to tell him about Jock, who was home but still recovering, and that Jimmy was dead. She let him think it had been old age. He had also loved the old cat. She told him about the mysterious shooting at the Hoggesses, but not about her troubles with them.

They were working in the garden when Charley and Dale pulled in.

"Hey, Tommy," Charley called as they got out. "Glad to hear they let you out. You're looking good."

"How's it going Charley?" They shook hands.

"Heard you're some sort of local hero," Dale said. He stood with his feet braced apart and his thumbs hooked in his equipment belt. "Football and track star, and all that. Hear you're a real hotshot with guns, too." He eyed Tommy belligerently. "A real super sniper. We don't need any fast guns running around the county."

"Where'd you find *him*, Charley?"

"He's new. Not quite broken in yet. Settle down Dale. Tommy's one of the good guys." Charley stared at the deputy until Dale shoved his hands in his pockets, and muttered an apology.

"By the way, Sue Ann. We finally found out who the other guy with the Hoggesses was. FBI identified him as a hit man for the drug ring. Seems the Hog's had done something to tick them off, and he was sent to make an object lesson of them. Just his bad luck the lab blew up with him in it. The lab was able to match his gun to the one intact bullet we recovered."

"Sounds like they made their own bed. What's going to happen to Jane and the kids?"

"She's went into rehab, but it didn't take. She's already back out on the street. Put the kids up for adoption. A real nice family is going to take them both."

"That's good to hear. I was worried about them, losing their whole family that way."

"Best thing that ever happened to those kids. Best for everyone else, too. We don't need any more Hoggesses running around."

"Amen, Charley." She slipped her arm around Tommy's waist. "Amen to that."

INSPIRATIONAL (SPIRITUAL/RELIGIOUS)

THE SONG OF THE SAW-WHET OWL

EDWARD A. HARA

Albert heard the sound as he was watching the sun paint streaks of pink across dark evening clouds. It was a high pitched peeping, in regular intervals. It went up one note in pitch for ten seconds, then stopped.

"What's that?" he asked.

"Northern Saw-whet owl. Pretty, isn't it?" Joanna cupped her hands to the sides of her mouth and perfectly imitated the call. There was silence for a few seconds, then the call repeated, louder and more urgent this time. She smiled. "He thinks I'm another male, challenging him for territory and mating rights." "How did you learn that?" "I sat here and listened at night. They only call during mating season. The rest of the year they are quiet and deadly little hunters."

"Little?"

"Oh, yes. He could fit nicely in the palm of your hand."

Albert tried to imagine an owl so small it would fit nicely in his hand.

"It's so beautiful here tonight. It's a shame you can't see it."

"I have my memories. I see everything clearly." She laughed. "I just have to close my eyes."

It was a joke. A joke because she was blind and her eyes would not open. Blind and terribly scarred from the acid that her ex-husband had thrown in her face when she discovered he was cheating on her. She confronted him in the garage late one night and a furious argument ensued. In anger he reached without looking for the nearest thing that he could find to throw at her. What his hand found was a bottle of acid he used to etch electronic circuit boards. His aim was perfect.

They sat in silence, enjoying the warmth of a late spring evening.

"I don't know how you ever forgave him for what he did to you."

"He asked me to forgive him." Joanna's voice was quiet and factual. "What else could I do?" "You *could* have told him to go straight to hell!" Albert growled, fidgeting with a cup of coffee on his lap. "That's what I would have told him. Straight to hell with you, pal!" There was another long silence. "How can you forgive someone for doing something like that to you?" His voice was subdued and filled with confusion.

"There is no *how*, Albert. You forgive. It's a choice, not a feeling."

The owl sang again. In the yard below, a cautious deer approached a feeding tub full of cracked corn. Albert leaned over and whispered in Joanna's ear, letting her know the deer was at the feeding tub.

They sat in silence until the doe left. Albert shook his head and sighed, his arms crossed over his chest.

"Weren't you angry with him?"

"Heavens, yes!" she sighed, rising from her seat. Her cane in hand, she tapped her way gently toward her back door. "It took me three weeks to call him back and forgive him after he called me from prison." They entered into the living roomand sat down together. She heard him plop down on one of her chairs and turned to the sound. "I didn't say it was easy, did I?"

"Okay, if it's a choice and not a feeling, how do you feel about him right now?"

The question caught her off guard. She really hadn't thought much about Mike since the day ten years ago that she had called him back and told him that she forgave him. He was in prison. She forgave him and life moved on.

She sat without speaking, facing straight ahead, her sightless eyes welded shut by scar tissue. Albert studied her as she sat with her thoughts, remembering the shock of first seeing her. He had come to repair her roof. When she met him at the door he was startled. She looked as if someone had ripped away the skin on her face in a brutal swatch from left to right across her eyes. This was what the acid had done, leaving a nasty looking red scar. As he watched, her fingers tightened on the cane and it began to tap on the floor. Harder and harder, until she gave it one last solid thump.

"I'm still mad at him," she managed to mutter. "God forgive me, I'm still mad at him."

"But you said you have forgiven him. How can you be mad at him?"

"I told you. Forgiveness is not a feeling." She rose from the chair and felt her way over to the kitchen counter. Working her way up the cabinets with her hands, she located her tea, found the tea kettle, and put it on the stove. Her hands deftly felt their way to the stove's knobs. She turned on the burner and waited to hear the *whoosh* of gas lighting. "It's something I have to do – between me and God. I forgive him every day. Every day I ask God to help me hold that forgiveness in my heart." She sighed deeply and lowered her head. "Some weeks it's one day at a time."

She turned and pointed to the wall of her living room. "Is my Crucifix there?" She didn't wait for an answer. "You know when I realized it wasn't going to be easy? After Mike called me. After he called I would think of that Crucifix every time I prayed. One night it occurred to me that it wasn't easy for God to forgive us either. Look at what it cost Him. Not easy. I kept praying for three weeks after he called me. Every time I prayed I swear a voice was telling me, *'I didn't say it was going to be easy, did I?'* " Albert rose from his chair slowly. "I should get going. It's getting late."

"No story?"

He hesitated, his hand on the doorknob. It was their routine whenever he came over. He would read from one of her books. She was still not comfortable with Braille. He had begun to read to her after she told him one night how much she missed reading her books. They were halfway through The Wind in the Willows.

"Not tonight."

"That's not like you, Albert. Is something wrong?"

"No," he lied. "I just need to get going. Can I give you a little kiss?" He went to her and kissed

her on the forehead. She gave him a smile in return.

"I like you, Albert." She reached out to touch his arms, then let her hands slide down their sides till she could take his hands in hers. "You're a nice man. Always remember that. You're my friend and I like you."

He liked her, too. Much more than he wanted to admit or could get the courage to tell her.

***

A week later he was still pondering their conversation and thinking of his brother. Dave, who thought the next dollar was the only thing life was about. Who had somehow managed to get their father's will changed and cheat him out of half a million dollars. It had been five years since Albert found out that Dave had done this to him. Five years and one punch in the mouth before walking angrily out of Dave's house. Yeah, he had sucker punched Dave real good. Laid him right out on that fancy carpet of his. Then, for good measure, Albert cussed him out, sparing nothing, before slamming the door on his way out.

He bent over a cup of coffee, shook his head slowly from side to side, and sighed. Wind whipped rain in crazy circles around the parking lot of the diner where he was eating breakfast. No roofing to be done today. How do you forgive someone who ruined your life? His life wasn't exactly ruined, but he could imagine a whole different life with that money. But Joanna. To never again see the moon shimmering across the tops of pine trees on a summer's eve. To never again see sunrises and sunsets over the ocean. To miss all the brilliant Spring flowers. His fists clenched in anger at the unfairness of it.

He let his mind wander back over time. Scenes flashed like photographic stills. Standing with Dave in the outfield of the old ballpark behind St. Mary's parish. Playing with a beach ball on the beach of St. Augustine. Christmas. Birthdays. Dave had always been his buddy. When did Dave change? What would make him do such a thing to his own brother? He tried to push the thoughts away, but they refused to go.

One of his workers approached.

"We no be work today?"

"No, Miguel. Sin el trabajo de hoy." He made a half saluting motion to the young man waiting at the edge of the table for a reply. Miguel turned and started to walk away. Albert called to him. "Miguel! Papel, por favor." Maybe reading the paper would get his mind off his brother. The paper was days old. Miguel read newspapers to learn English. It was a small town paper, full of the usual small town stuff. Not like the Miami Herald where he had grown up. He looked at the dreary day outside. Would be nice to be in Florida now. He hated the weather in the Northwest. Always seemed to be raining.

LOCAL WOMAN KILLED IN FALL.

Another tragedy. He scanned the story, only half interested and ready to throw the paper in the corner and go home. Maybe he would go see Joanna later. They could talk. She might help him understand.

His hands suddenly clenched the paper as he read. He uttered a loud, guttural cry, half moan and half scream of denial. It pierced the air, causing people to turn and look his way.

"Joanna! No, no, no!" He slammed the paper on the table and continued to moan, his face buried in his hands. As a nearby diner tentatively arose from his seat to offer help, Albert thrust himself from the table and dashed out the door.

***

He pushed aside the police tape and used a credit card to jimmy the front door. The house was cool and damp. He ran through the rooms, calling her name frantically, as if his insistent calling could somehow make her appear in the living room. He kept screaming out her name until he collapsed onto her living room sofa, unable to cry, unable to speak in the searing reality of her death.

After a while, he openedtheback doorandwalked slowly outonto thedeck. A section of therailing was missing. He stared numbly, then shuffled over to examine it. The wood was rotten. He peered over the edge. The offending section still lay on the ground where it had carried her to her death. As he lifted his eyes again, he saw the grave. It was still fresh, the dirt settled down by the morning rain.

She had always said she was going to be buried in her backyard, even going to war with the township untilthey relented andgave herpermission. Hiseyes examined thegrave. A large andplain stone said: Joanna Perkins. November 7, 1959 – April 25, 2012. "But the greatest of these is love" 1 Corinthians 13:13. Her daughters had kept their promise.

He thought of the many times he had come over and found her standing at the railing, facing the woods she could not see, taking in the sounds and smells of the forest behind her home. She must have leaned forward. The wood was no good. She must have leaned forward. The wood was no good. Leaned forward. The wood was no good. Leaned forward. Leaned forward. Leaned forward. He shook his head and groaned, trying to purge the image of her falling.

When he looked up, a flash of movement startled him, followed by a soft thump. A small, gray ball of feathers lay on the deck in front of the door. It was a bird of some sort. As Albert approached, the bird flapped around in fear, trying to get to its feet. Disoriented, it tried to take off and slammed again into the glass of the door.

Albert was on it quickly. Covering it with his hands, he pulled it close to the warmth of his chest, trying to calm it. The bird resisted for a couple of seconds, then went still. He cautiously opened his hands. It was an owl. An owl so small it fit nicely in the palm of his hand. He opened his hands a little more. The owl did not move. He poked it tentatively with his finger, then realized it was dead.

He shook his head. There were words but no sense. The world was crazy. Was he hearing voices in his head?

"I didn't say it was easy, did I?"

He went inside the house and found one of Joanna's shirts still in her closet. He wrapped the owl in the shirt and went down the steps to her grave. A few swipes with a shovel made a nice size hole. He placed the owl in the hole and replaced the dirt. He stood and stared at the grave for a few minutes, then walked back to his truck. He plucked his cell phone out of its holder and began to dial.

"I didn't say it was easy, did I?"

When the voice on the other end said hello he replied, "Davy? It's Albert. I forgive you." There was no answer. After a long time with no reply, he flipped the phone shut. Turning back to the house, he entered the side door to the garage and began to rummage around. He found a Jerry can, half filled with gas. He trudged down the hallway, studying the house as he walked through it. She never taken his name off the deed to the house, even after what he had done. Why?

"I didn't say it was easy, did I?"

"Shut up!" Albert growled. He didn't want to hear it. Let her forgive him. He would make sure some small bit of justice prevailed in a senseless universe. The can tilted in his hands. The pungent smell of gasoline filled the room.

"I didn't say it was easy, did I?"

Albert's hand paused. A single drop of gas poised on the nozzle, then splashed on the floor. Through the silence came a high pitched peeping sound, set at close intervals. It went up one note in pitch for ten seconds, then stopped. His hand tightened on the handle, then he screamed and blindly flung the can. It crashed through the thin glass of the window behind him and bounced across the deck.

Hours later the police found Albert at Joanna's grave. He was sleeping, his body slumped against the headstone. The sergeant shook his head, trying to understand. There was an odd hole dug in the grave. The sleeping man was holding a small dead owl in his hands, pressed against his heart.

GREEK GODDESS OF KITCHEN AND BLOCK

Marisa Churchill wields a whisk as well as a mean breaststroke.

BY ELAINE K. HOWLEY

With long, dark braids swinging from beneath a patterned cap, Marisa Churchill leaps into action. A clock in the corner ticks off the seconds in bold, digital numbers. Time is moving almost as swiftly as Churchill as she careens from one end of the kitchen to the other, hands laden with ingredients and implements. She's five episodes into the second season of cable network Bravo's reality series *Top Chef,* and her future on the dramatic cooking program is on the line.

Rather than sweating the challenge at hand— to create the fifth of six courses at a social luncheon for a celebrity client— she relaxes into the tension and plows ahead, a feeling she equates with the urgency she has experienced so often on the starting block at dozens of Masters swim meets over the past several years.

"I'm someone who really enjoys working under pressure. That's an asset of mine that was really helpful for me," the California Culinary Academy (CCA) graduate says of her time on the hit series in 2006. And it's a skill her swimming has helped hone.

"If you're used to having to get up on the starting blocks and be under that pressure and have people staring at you, and the clocks— Are you going to make the time you want?; Are you going to screw up your turns?; those sorts of things— I think it makes it easier to get used to a situation where you have 20 minutes to make an *amuse bouche* and you have to get the ingredients out of the vending machine and then there's a camera man in your face asking you 20 questions," she says, referencing the "Quickfire Challenge" from Episode Four.

Despite her cool under pressure, Churchill was eliminated in the fifth episode. The judges didn't care for the high-concept intermezzo course she concocted with her challenge partner, Josie, who was also eliminated that day. Gracefully, Churchill bid her fellow competitors farewell and left the show. What had started as her big break had apparently come screeching to a halt.

But fast-forward five years, and Churchill, now 34, is enjoying a continued steady rise within the culinary world. A new dessert cookbook confirms her arrival on the scene and a score of happy Masters teammates are asking for more of her yummy treats.

SWIMMING SWEETLY

In addition to being a nationally-recognized pastry chef who has worked at several of the top restaurants in foodie-town San Francisco including The Slanted Door, Ame, and Lulu, Churchill is also an accomplished Masters swimmer.

Despite her seemingly swimming-chiseled physique, Churchill only started swimming competitively within the past decade. "I got into a car accident about eight or nine years ago and my doctor prescribed swimming as physical therapy and I just fell in love with it," she says. She took some lessons from Alison Wagner, a former Olympian-turned coach, and with Wagner's encouragement, Churchill took the plunge and joined the University of San Francisco Masters team. She was a natural.

"I'm tall, I have big hands and big feet, and I was lucky to find the sport I love," she says.

"I always wish I'd discovered it sooner, but a lot of times, you talk to people who've been swimming forever, they get really burnt out on it, so from that perspective, I'm glad that I found it when I did. I just love it and I don't think I'll ever get burnt out from it. It's a nice therapy."

Although still somewhat new to swimming, Churchill competed at the Short Course

Yards Masters Nationals meet in Coral Gables, FL in May, 2006. She finished in the top 10 in both the 100 breaststroke and 50 butterfly events. "That's my claim to fame," she says with a chuckle.

The 100 breaststroke also happens to be Churchill's favorite event. With breaststroke, she can capitalize on her strong kick without the hindrance of an upper body that she says, "doesn't do a whole lot for me. I'm all legs, all kick, and very flexible. That makes me somebody who's good for breaststroke."

JOURNEY TO BECOMING AMERICA'S NEXT GREAT CHEF

Churchill grew up in a Greek household in Arizona and eventually came to California to pursue a career as a chef. Her grandmother was a big influence on her interest in food, and Greek cuisine features heavily in the foods Churchill prepares. After attending the prestigious CCA, Churchill later attended the Culinary Institute of America at Greystone to further her pastry skills. She worked her way up the restaurant ladder earning the respect of food critics and the local press in San Francisco.

"I'd been listed as one of the top pastry chefs in the city by food critic Michael Bauer, and people knew I was interested in [being on *Top Chef*]. Ironically, the first person who told me about the show was Alison Wagner." A second friend of Churchill's—another Masters swimmer—also mentioned it to her. "After a couple people said it, I thought, 'Hmmm, maybe there's something to this.'"

She was working at Ame Restaurant at the time, and co-owners Lisa Doumani and Hiro Sone had been guest judges on *Top Chef: Season 1*. "I watched [a video of the episode] and went online and saw they were doing a casting call, so I just decided to go try out for it."

Churchill mustered a calm confidence when auditioning and her straight-forward tactic worked. The audition did not require that Churchill cook for any casting agents or judges.

"No, c'mon! Top Chef is all about the drama!" she laughs. "I knew they were looking for a pastry chef, so I showed up [at the audition] in a tight pair of jeans, brought in some chocolates, and said, 'I'm your pastry chef.'" The casting agents agreed, and she was offered a spot on the second season of the now-iconic cooking show.

Every episode features two challenges—a time-limited, off-the-wall "Quickfire Challenge," that simply determines which chef will have "immunity" from elimination during that episode's second and higher-stakes "Elimination Challenge." The loser of that second challenge endures an inquest by a panel of judges and is ultimately removed from the show and competition for a range of prizes including $100,000 by the statuesque model and cookbook author, Padma Lakshmi, with her signature demand that the contestant, "pack your knives and go." It's an intense environment wired for drama.

"I packed a swimsuit and goggles for when I went on the show. I was hoping for the opportunity to swim, but *Top Chef* is brutal that way. You're in total lock down. There's no time and you're not allowed to go do anything like that. You're either doing the competition or you're back at the dorms for a couple hours of sleep. There's no cell phone, no television, no gym, no pool. That was really tough."

Churchill estimates less than three-quarters of what makes it onto an episode is "reality."

"I've gotten in trouble for saying this before, but it's amazing what can happen in the editing room. What you see is about 65% to 70% reality. The rest is just editing. They can create what they want," during the editing process, she says, a form of near-scripting after the fact that often means comments and interactions are taken out of context and moved around to fit whatever storyline the producers want to present.

While that may be true of the interpersonal drama that is the hallmark of reality TV, Churchill insists that the challenge sequences are not treated to the same editorial creativity. "When you have 20 minutes for the challenge, or you're just learning about the ingredients you can use right then, that is true. You really do have just 20 minutes." The only real editing that happens to the challenge sequences is the insertion of piecetocamera interviews that are actually taped after the challenge is over and spliced in as realtime narration.

SWEET & SKINNY

Top Chef opened doors for Churchill, one of them being the release of her new cookbook, *Sweet & Skinny: 100 Recipes for Enjoying Life's Sweeter Side without Tipping the Scales* published by Clarkson Potter in 2011.

Churchill landed the book deal through careful consideration of the needs of the market and leverage of her growing fame. She worked with a literary agent to find the eager imprint, a division of Random House. "Clarkson Potter liked the concept of the book so much they put a rush on it. Where most cookbooks are written in a year or more, I had five-and-a-half months to write this one." That condensed timeline meant Churchill was full-time focused on perfecting her recipes and moving the project forward.

They say it takes a village to raise a child, and for Churchill, her cookbook wouldn't have come to fruition without the help of her swimming village. During the recipe development phase, Churchill whipped up batches of various recipes and brought them to practice for feedback. A few of her teammates went a step further and became recipe testers to make sure her directions were clear and logical. Churchill is a fan favorite at meets, bringing plenty of Peanut Butter and Jelly Cookies and Apricot Bars to share. Both recipes pack well and keep for a few days, and make an ideal pre-race snack, she says.

With her book, Churchill hopes to fill a distinct need for tasty desserts with less sugar, fat, and calories. As a paid spokesperson for Truvia, Churchill endorses the use of the natural, stevia-based sweetener in her recipes and many of the recipes in her book can be made sugar-free by simply replacing sugar with Truvia.

NEXT LAP

In addition to touring in support of her cookbook, Churchill is also collaborating on a line of *Sweet & Skinny* products and "hopefully working on another cookbook. We need to cover breakfast!" she says, ticking off a list of muffins, scones, and granola dishes she wants to spin skinny.

All of these current and future endeavors were made possible by her participation on *Top Chef*, she says. "Getting involved with the Food Network challenges, becoming the spokesperson for Truvia, writing the cookbook… all these things were made possible in part by *Top Chef*," she says of the highly-productive, if isolating, three weeks she spent fighting for survival on the show.

For Marisa Churchill, her future potential as a chef, cookbook writer, celebrity, and
swimmer appears to be as sky high as her meringues.

Elaine K. Howley is a freelance journalist and open water swimmer hailing from **the Boston area. She enjoys the cold water in New England (yes, really!) and was the** 32nd swimmer to complete the Triple Crown of open water marathon swimming.

SILENT MOVIES

JOON-JI HAN

Silence. The wind wove its way through the tall willow trees, leaving behind a trail of its autumnal perfume in its well-trodden path. Fallen leaves of all colours, from brown to orange to yellow to gold, rose to dance briefly with the gust of wind before it spirited away in search for a new partner. I closed my eyes and inhaled, sending the fresh, crisp air cascading down my throat and into my lungs. It left a tangerine tang on my tongue, overlaid with the bitter taste of tree bark. It tasted of autumn.

I opened my eyes and stretched, loosening the muscles that had stiffened after hours of sitting slouched against the tree. The leaves hanging precariously above my head cast a golden buttery glow under the light of the setting sun. Twirling the chewed-on pencil in my fingers, I studied the sketchpad resting on my lap. Harsh, black lines stood slanted in many directions, like an army of exhausted soldiers. Small graphite leaves of grey patterned the floor and the air around the tree trunks. I glanced up at my surroundings, then back at my sketchpad. No resemblance. A sigh escaped my lips.

Something vibrated in my pocket. I fished my phone out, catching the sketchpad in time before it fell onto the cold earth.

Dinner's ready. Love, Dad.

Lips stretching into a grin, I tossed my sketchpad and pencil into my backpack and stood up. A sudden gust of wind blew my black hair into a frenzy, and I reached up to push it out of my eyes. *That hair of yours is going to be the death of you someday.* I suppressed a smile as I remembered what dad had said as he played with my long hair. Shouldering my bag, I began to trudge through the piles of leaves toward the path that would lead me back to the main park.

I watched as a single leaf fluttered noiselessly to the ground before me. I finally reached the main area of the park. A couple strolled through an array of trees, linked hands swinging between them. An elderly woman sat on a nearby bench, throwing some crumbs of bread to the gathering pigeons. A mother watched as her little boy ran through the leaves, sending them spiraling into the air. A group of guys I recognized from my school was walking toward me. One of them, the one with the jaunty saunter, opened his mouth to speak. Even from the distance, I could read his lips.

Hey, it's the deaf girl.

***

Douglas Fairbanks Jr. threw his head back and laughed as he escaped yet another one of his foes. I laughed along with him, inhaling the mouth-watering smell of popcorn drenched in butter. I grabbed the pencil that never left my side and found a piece of paper. I scrawled, *The actors are ridiculously melodramatic.*

Dad picked it up and smiled, the corners of his eyes etched with crow's feet. He took the pencil from my hand and replied in his large, messy handwriting, *That's why silent movies are so fun to watch. How do you like* The Thief of Baghdad *so far?*

It's alright. I liked Birth of a Nation *better.*

Me too. Fairbanks is such a horrible actor it's a wonder they didn't just shoot him then and there.

I looked up at dad, who was leaning back in his favourite recliner, and feigned a shocked expression. He waggled his thick eyebrows. I smothered another laugh and continued watching the beat-up T.V set, snuggling into the lime green threadbare couch. I smoothed the paper in my hands, feeling the bumps caused by graphite pressing down onto it. Dad always "spoke" with writing. When he was still teaching me how to read lips, he'd had to communicate using hand gestures. Unfortunately, he's not the best at charades.

On the screen, Fairbanks was confessing his love to the heroine, hands pressed to his heart. I grimaced, but inside I felt my heart go all funny. Sure, it was cheesy, but every teenage girl has her dreams.

Wrapped in a cocoon spun out of warmth and satisfaction, I fought against my heavy eyelids as they drooped lower and lower. Outside, the moon hung low in the dark night sky while glittering stars mingled with the skyscrapers of New York. The soft spring breeze slipped in through the open window, hand-in-hand with the faint smell of hot dogs. Dad gingerly plucked the pencil out of my grip, reached for another piece of paper, and started scribbling on it. Pure silence swayed in the air on whisper-thin threads.

Finally, I let sleep take me away in her gentle caress. Only after I woke up, a warm woolen blanket draped over me, would I read what dad had scrawled on the paper. *These movies are even greater because you and I both can equally enjoy it to its full extent. Love you.*

Black and white movies have no sound. It was then that I realized that dad's gift to me was something precious. It was the gift of not having to stand apart from the others, of not being different just because I was deaf. It was the gift of belonging.

***

The temperature was dropping, fast. I pulled my sweater tighter around myself, and hurried toward the direction of the park entrance. I kept my head down, eyes trained on my grey Converses. *Please don't let them follow me. Please, please, please.*

A pair of dirt-stained sneakers appeared before me. I looked up and swallowed. It was the boy with the saunter. Behind him stood his friends, all looking uncomfortable.

I ground my teeth together and raised an eyebrow.

"Where ya going?" The boy stood with his hands shoved in his pockets, a smirk plastered onto his face.

"Home."

"So deaf girl can talk, huh?"

Having to read his lips was not a pleasant task. They were cracked, and he constantly kept licking them against the dry air.

Stifling a groan, I tried to walk past him. He mirrored my movements.

My heart was pounding in my chest. I glanced desperately at the entrance. It wasn't that far away. If I ran...

He grinned at me. I glared back. He stepped closer. I held my ground.

Someone put a hand on his shoulder. It was a green-eyed boy with dark brown hair. "Rick, leave her alone. Let's go."

I seized the opportunity and quickly walked away. I stopped and turned around. The boy was looking at me, a worried look in his eyes. I mouthed, *Thanks.* He smiled.

When I was a safe block away from the park, I leaned against a bricked wall and unclenched my fists. Little crescent moons winked at me from my palms. I waited until they disappeared.

The questions sliced through my mind, leaving papercuts, raw and shallow, inside of me. Why me? Why do people like them have to pick on people like me? If I wasn't the way I am now, if I wasn't deaf, would they still act like this?

The tears that came were unbidden, and I stared at a yellow car parked by the curb until they subsided. *This isn't the first time something like that's happened,* I told myself as I shouldered my backpack and began walking home. *You'll be fine.*

Above, the streetlights flickered to life, one by one.

When I unlocked the familiar yellow door and tossed my backpack onto the familiar wooden floor, the smell of buttered popcorn wafted over to me. I saw dad readying the television set. I knew I was home.

NATURAL SCIENCE

RANDY OSBOURNE

By the time I reached the dog, the rising tidewater was almost up to his neck. Neither of us could swim, and I was afraid we both might drown.

The dog was Dante, a 140-pound Irish wolfhound who belonged to my writer girlfriend from Colorado. The lagoon was in Bolinas, a seaside town north of San Francisco, where we lived for a few months so that she could teach. Dante had raised his leg to pee on a traffic sign at the bend in Wharf Road. Woozy from that morning's chemo, he toppled from the retaining wall just as the tide began to come in.

I ran to the dock at the Rod & Boat Club. Removed my watch and wallet. Pulled off my shoes. Eased into the water.

The Pacific Ocean is colder than anyone expects. My scrotum tightened like a fist, and every internal organ was looking for a place to hide. At first I felt the sand like firm, rippled pudding on the soles of my feet. Then my feet went numb, my legs went numb, everything went numb.

I thought: So this is how it feels. Or doesn't feel.

*

A few years earlier, my father had become a paraplegic after an accident in his home. I hadn't seen him in decades; he left town after the divorce, when I was six. But I retrieved him from the hospital and got him installed at a special home in Georgia, where I was living at the time.

My father could no longer hunt, fish or chase women. They wouldn't let him drink, either. At every visit, he begged me for a gun. "If you don't, I'll get one some other way. I can." I kept dreaming up new ways to distract him from the subject, derail the usual conversation. Once, I told him that I had a friend who was pregnant and thinking about an abortion. She needed advice. What should I tell her?

This was a lie. I had seen a headline that morning about RU-486, the abortion pill, soon to be legalized. In 1999, RU-486 was all over the news. My father said, "It's not the worst thing. Your mother had an abortion when you were two years old. She took care of it."

The floral-papered walls of Peachtree Manor seemed to fall away from me. I said, "Took care of it? Took care of it how? I was two years old in 1957. Roe v. Wade didn't come around until the year I graduated high school."

My father shrugged. How she took care of it didn't matter. Only a gun mattered to him now. We argued.

This is unfair, I told him. All those years without you, and now I find you, and you only want me to help you die. Not only unfair, but also abnormal. Or unnatural, if natural is how life goes until we try to make it normal.

I was being unfair to him, too. He simply wanted to close out for good the riddle of his loneliness, a need I understand now. Men get divorced and leave town and go wandering. They abandon their children. It happens all the time; it's what I did. Which is how I ended up in Bolinas, with a girlfriend and her dog, Dante, who fell into the lagoon.

*

Dante stood there shivering. He couldn't move, with a big bandage on his front leg where they had put the bolts and pins. Bone cancer.

I moved slowly toward him in the water, which was at his neck. I curled my arm under him, lifted, pulled him along. He whimpered. The water was now almost to my own collarbone. Dante growled, low in his throat.

Then he went berserk.

He barked and yapped and swung around, thrashing at me with his paws. He scored a blow in my face with that bandage. I went under, popped up again. He went under. I hoisted him. At last I achieved a sort of modified half nelson, and Dante quit struggling. We made it to the dock and with a mighty oomph, I heaved him onto it. Dante stood, swaying. As I hauled myself onto the dock, he collapsed, panting, and then I collapsed beside him, the wooden planks warm against my cheeks, from the sun.

Dante's cancer spread. The experimental surgery to save his paw didn't work, and his leg was amputated. He died, and so did my father. With a box of his ashes, I ended up living on the other side of Mt. Tamalpais from Bolinas, in a little town called Mill Valley.

I loved that green mountain as much as I'd loved the craggy peaks of Colorado, where the girlfriend had introduced me to her friend, Eric, a filmmaker. Eric was up in the mountains to direct an emotionally complex western. At dinner, Eric told me the story of how he had lost his brother to AIDS, how he had scattered his brother's ashes in their favorite boyhood creek, early one winter in upstate New York, and returned the following week for a visit. "I rounded a bend, and there he was – my brother," Eric said. A tree had fallen across the creek. The ashes had not dispersed well, and were "congealed, hardened against the side of that tree, like an obscene, petrified sponge," Eric said. "I wanted … I wanted to gather him up."

I would do a better job scattering my father's ashes. After his death, I learned from one of his early wives that he had said he did not want to live past 50. But he had lived to a miserable old age, both legs amputated because of bedsores. He developed leukemia. His kidneys failed. I could give him this, at least.

At first I planned to distribute his ashes in the rivers and streams where he fished, but then I figured, why not the ocean? This is where they all end up. On my 50th birthday, I drove over Mt. Tamalpais to the beach in Bolinas.

I had a fantasy of how this would happen. Ever since Dad told me about the abortion, I had pictured my mother's unborn fetus as a boy – my little brother. Somehow, in my mind at least, we would do this together. My brother would carry the box ashes to the water. I would open it and fling them, set them free. As the older brother I would try to pray, but I don't pray very well, and so he would pray for us. He might fall to his knees, as he finished the prayer. I would gather him up.   Of course, the day didn't go that way. My grown son Skyler was visiting, and we rode together to the beach at Bolinas, at an hour when I knew the tide would be going out. We watched the frigid Pacific waves furl the ashes away.

Skyler said, "What's that?" He pointed to a dark blob, farther up the beach and we ran to it, grateful for something else to do. The baby sea lion honked and squawked and flapped at dry sand. Its black disc eyes, rimmed with spiky lashes, stared at us.

I phoned the marine biology center. The woman said, "You did the right thing by not touching him. He will either make it back to the ocean by himself, or the tide will come up and get him. This is normal." She skipped mentioning a third possibility, and I think she meant "natural."

Leaving Bolinas, I called out landmarks to my son. "There's the house where I used to live. And Smiley's Saloon. I spent plenty of time in Smiley's. And there's the Rod & Boat Club," which had even less significance to him. As we passed, I glanced toward the dock. I saw – or I think I saw; I'm pretty sure I saw – a fading, irregular, more or less dog-shaped stain.

ETHEREAL EXISTENCE

CLAIRE ELIZABETH SCHERZINGER

It's raining little pebbles falling into a stone garden
As we walk,
Further into black-haired people and some bone-bleach white.
School uniforms rushing past like little Japanese *gaki*
Sweeping the dead spirits off the streets.

Sometimes I feel my existence is ethereal
When I am helping you up to the washroom at 3 am
And one side of you is immobile as the trays of ice cubes I keep in
the freezer.

You are the one I always imagine being with in Kyoto
Our steps making little ringing noises, stepping on a xylophone
As we walk past pagodas with men playing grand pianos in them.

When I imagined the future with you it was an alternative soundtrack
Playing in the background,
One with lots of synthesizers and low humming cellos
And a woman looking out a window on a rainy day.
She sits at her stainless steel Ikea kitchen set.
Her sad and happy smile—a long awaited death in the family.

My life with you would be cinematic. A film with desaturated tones—
greys impregnating the whites.

And now
Kyoto
This is a place where we can do work on the other:
Walking under lacquered red pillars
With umbrellas that have transparent membranes
To shield our old and weary skin from the rain.
The corners of our mouths unfurling,
Our eyes slowly stretching out like a book cracked open.
Making lips touch for the last time
And swallowing the moistness of dewy skin on a cold day.

You may not think this is woman's work,
But goodbyes are giving birth to a feeling that tastes like bitter green tea
And is the constant rubbing under the eyes that makes us grow old
too fast.

PAINTED POSTCARD FROM JAPAN, 1944

MICHELLE PEREZ

She strolls past the village shops carrying the snow
umbrella. Kimono layers keep her warm—silk red,
while vague snowflakes swim around her, settle low
over thatched roofs, on top of the parasol spread
taut, at a slight tilt, that she holds aloft.

Dim windows light her path, for the sun, nearly set,
dips into mauve and tan mountains. The hillside air,
crystalline, forms an idyllic, carefree backdrop—yet,
close beneath the proud umbrella her satin hair
belies a sadness, pinned with blossoms ruby soft.

But no one sees her pass unless they happen to glance
outside. *All's safe* they must think or perhaps, by chance,
they catch a glimpse of life this artist left undone.

For there is something lost in her aloneness, almost
captured in the blurred wash of wood houses: a ghost-
like curtain, one organdy cloud… the fading sun.

HELEN OF SPARTA

JACOB M. APPEL

4 FEMALE / 3 MALE

This retelling of Homer's *Iliad* from the point of view of Helen of Troy begins when the Trojan prince, Paris, after a casual fling with the Spartan queen, Helen, abducts his lover and carries her off to Troy. Unfortunately for Paris, Helen turns out to be far more difficult than he imagined—for example, refusing to consume foods that begin with any letter other than "Z." While Paris is scouring the kingdom for zucchini, Helen falls under the sway of Paris's cynical, hard-drinking first wife, Oenone, who convinces Helen to make Paris a *quid pro quo* offer: She will fall in love with him—in return for the deed to the entire kingdom of Troy. When Paris protests that he is not heir to Troy—that he has two older brothers standing to inherit—Helen insists that Paris view them not as brothers but as "impediments." If he truly wants her love, he must slaughter his brothers in order to prove his devotion.

Meanwhile, the middle-aged Phylacean king, Protesilaus, has launched an expedition to retrieve Helen from the Trojans. Despite the pleas of his neurotic wife, Laodamia, who warns him that the first Greek to step foot on Trojan soil is prophesied to die in battle, Protesilaus insists on taking the risk so that "school children in three thousand years will recite the name Protesilaus with awe and wonder." He enlists Paris's doomsaying sister, Cassandra, to assure his wife that they are in no danger. A second rescue expedition, mounted by Helen's husband, Menelaus, runs into immediate difficulties when the Spartan king finds himself on the Pan-Hellenic do-not-sail list.

Helen of Sparta tells a contemporary story of love and loss through the lens of a classical myth. The work is intended as a bittersweet romantic comedy with strong feminist overtones that forces the viewer to rethink a careworn but beloved tale of antiquity.

CHARACTERS IN THE PLAY

4 FEMALE / 3 MALE

Helen of Sparta	The world's most beautiful woman. **(F-20s)**
Paris	A Trojan prince. Madly in love with Helen. **(M-20s)**
Oenone	Wife of Paris. Jilted and jaded. **(F-20s)**
Cassandra / Chorus	A bearer of tidings, some true. **(F-20s)**
Menelaus	King of Sparta, Helen's husband. **(M-30s)**
Protesilaus	King of the Phylaceans. **(M-45-60)**
Laodamia	Wife of Protesilaus. **(F-45-60)**

TIME & PLACE

This play is intended to be an exploration of myth and fantasy....

A NOTE ON SUBTITLES

The subtitles/scene headings are intended to be either projected or read aloud. Successful productions will experiment with these headings and may choose to present them selectively or even to alter them as necessary.

A NOTE ON THE VOICE OF THE GODS

The gods are called upon to speak on several occasions during the course of this play. Please keep in mind that these are benevolent, generous gods, who volunteer their time because they are sincerely trying to be helpful.

ACT ONE

1. Troy. A hilltop. Helen and Paris. Then Cassandra.

(Paris enters, carrying Helen over his shoulder. Helen is bound hand-and-foot and gagged. Paris sets her down, leaning her against a tree or wall, as necessary.)

PARIS
Behold! Troy.
(Paris waits for Helen's reaction. She says nothing.)
Pretty impressive, huh?

HELEN
(Through her gag)
Mmmph!

PARIS
I guess I can take that off you now...but please don't start shouting again....

HELEN
Mmmph! Mmmmmmph—
(Paris removes her gag.)
—claw your goddam eyes out!

PARIS
(Ignoring Helen's outburst, focused on the view)
Well? What do you think?

HELEN
Honestly, it looks so...suburban.

PARIS

Pastoral.

HELEN

PARIS
Trust me on this one, Helen. The schools are excellent. It's safe to walk a dog late at night. When we retire, we'll be able to raise tomatoes in our own garden....Did I mention that the schools are excellent?

HELEN
I don't like dogs. Or tomatoes.

PARIS
Not yet.

HELEN
I'm hungry.

PARIS
I'll be back in a moment. Don't go anywhere.
    (Calling off stage.)
Cassandra...! Cassandra...!
    (Paris walks to the corner of the stage in search of his sister.
    Cassandra enters, pushing a wheelbarrow full of pears.)

PARIS
You've got the pears!

CASSANDRA
These are just the Bartletts and the Boscs. I left the Forelles and the Red Anjous at the bottom of the hill....But I'm telling you, this is not going to work.

PARIS
That's *your* opinion.

CASSANDRA
I know what I'm taking about, Paris. Only *one* pear. And tempt her with it.

PARIS

What kind of woman is impressed by only *one* pear?

CASSANDRA
You're not trying to impress her—you're trying to make her fall in love with you. There's a difference.

PARIS
I bet she hasn't seen this many pears in her entire life.
(Paris takes several pears from the barrow and juggles.)

CASSANDRA
If impressive were the same as romantic, men would weep to death over female shotputters.... The reality is that good courting is like good fishing. First you get the hook in and then you run in the opposite direction.

PARIS
That doesn't sound very romantic.

CASSANDRA
The romance comes *later*. In taking the hook out together. In tending to the wound.... But do you know what *you're* doing with all these pears? You're running *at* her—and you don't have a hook in yet.

PARIS
I was trained as a shepherd, not a fisherman.

CASSANDRA
I hate to break this to you, big brother, but what works on sheep doesn't always work on women....

PARIS
We'll see about that....Do you want to meet your future sister-in-law?

CASSANDRA
You're already married. And so is she.

PARIS
Keep your voice down.

(Paris leads Cassandra to Helen.)
Helen, darling. This is my baby sister, Cassandra.

CASSANDRA
It's so good to finally meet you....after everything Paris wrote about you in his letters.
(Cassandra extends her hand to shake Helen's, but Helen is bound and cannot reciprocate.)

HELEN
Did he mention the part about how he kidnapped me in the middle of the night—how he dragged me kicking and screaming out of my husband's bed?

PARIS
I told you I don't like that word. *Kidnapped.* Can't you humor me and say *rescued*?

HELEN
Nobody asked you to *rescue* me....

PARIS
(Paris opens his copy of "Romance for Dummies.")
It says right here that true love means doing things for your beloved without ever having to be asked....

HELEN
But I'm not your beloved....I hardly know you.....

PARIS
My grandparents went on three dates before they got married and they've been together for fifty years. My great-grandparents had an arranged marriage in the Old Country and they were together for sixty years.

HELEN
This is ludicrous. I have a husband back in Sparta. My husband is the *king* of Sparta.

PARIS

Please, darling. None of that. The key to a successful relationship is keeping focused on the future—never letting yourself dwell on the past....

HELEN

Goddammit! Once and for all, we are *not* having a relationship.

PARIS

Calm down, darling. Do you know what I've brought you?

HELEN

(Helen looks at the wheelbarrow full of pears)
Pears?

PARIS

Aren't you impressed? These are the finest pears in the entire kingdom.

HELEN

What am I going to do with a wheelbarrow full of pears?

PARIS

Eat them.

HELEN

I don't eat foods whose names begin with the letter P.

PARIS

You don't?

HELEN

I've *never* eaten foods that begin with P. Not since I was a little girl. No pears. No potatoes. No pasta.

CASSANDRA

I told you so.

PARIS

You did not. You said give her *one* pear. Even *one* pear begins with a P.

CASSANDRA
I said *tempt* her with one pear. I didn't say to give it to her....
Now do you want me to carry up the rest of that fruit, big
brother? I have ten more barrows.

PARIS
What I want to do is throw myself from the battlements in
despair.

CASSANDRA
Then I might as well leave the pears for you at the bottom of
the hill....

PARIS
(To Cassandra, exasperated.)
Keep the pears. She'll come around.

CASSANDRA
I'll make preserves....I wonder what Professor Schliemann
and his archeologists are going to think someday when they
unearth five thousand jars of pear jam....

PARIS
What are you blathering about?

CASSANDRA
Nothing. I'm just keeping focused on the future.
(Cassandra exits with the wheelbarrow.)

HELEN
Why do men always try to impress me with pears? Pears are
terribly impractical. They spoil easily. They stimulate indiges-
tion. In large doses, they cause cancer in rats....

PARIS
(To Helen)
In large enough doses, *everything* causes cancer in rats....Do
you know how hard it is to get pears out of season in the Ancient World? Can't you show some appreciation?

HELEN

I'm the most beautiful woman in the world. I don't have to
show any appreciation....

PARIS

You *are* the most beautiful woman in the world.

HELEN

And the hungriest.

PARIS

Okay, no more foods beginning with the letter P. How about
some fresh strawberries? Or a fillet of scrod? Steamed, not
poached.

HELEN

That's very sweet of you....But I don't eat foods that begin
with the letter S either.

PARIS

You've got to be joking.

HELEN

I don't mean to make things difficult. Honestly. Other than a
few first-letter preferences, I'm really not very picky....

PARIS

So how do you feel about apples?

HELEN

I have nothing against them....I just don't eat them.

PARIS

Bagels?

HELEN

Unfortunately, no.

PARIS

Carrots?

HELEN

Sorry.

PARIS
Duck à l'orange? Escargot? Fettuccini alfredo?

HELEN
Never. Never. Never.

PARIS
This is getting us nowhere. For God's sake: What *do* you eat?

HELEN
Foods that begin with the letter Z.

PARIS
Z?

HELEN
In Sparta, I dine every night on zebra cookies and Zamorano cheese and zwieback. Topped off with a glass of zinfandel.

PARIS
If I bring you zebra cookies and zinfandel, then will you fall in love with me?

HELEN
Let me put it this way. If you bring me zebra cookies and zinfandel, I won't go on a hunger strike.

2. Sparta. The Waterfront. Menelaus and Cassandra as Port Security Officer.

(*Cassandra, wearing the uniform of a port security officer,* stands before the gangplank of a warship. Menelaus, sporting travel clothes and a briefcase, waits opposite her. After a substantial pause, Cassandra looks up from a scroll of parchment.)

CASSANDRA AS PORT SECURITY OFFICER
I'm sorry, Your Majesty. Now is that Menelaus with an A or an E?

MENELAUS

King Menelaus. M-E-N-E-L-A-U-S.

CASSANDRA AS PORT SECURITY OFFICER
Oh. My husband has a cousin Menalaus—M-E-N-*A*-L-A-U-S—who sells anvils in Syracuse. I thought you might be related....

MENELAUS
Well, we're not.

CASSANDRA AS PORT SECURITY OFFICER
It could be a corruption, you know. Sometimes the same family spells a name in multiple ways, particularly if the older generation was illiterate....

MENELAUS
Nobody in my family is illiterate. Or sells anvils. Or lives in Syracuse. My father was a Greek king, and his father was a Greek king, and his father sat with the gods at Mount Olympus....You can trace our lineage all the way back to prehistoric times and even then none of us were illiterate....Say, how are you doing with that boarding pass?

CASSANDRA AS PORT SECURITY OFFICER

MENELAUS
What sort of glitch?

CASSANDRA AS PORT SECURITY OFFICER
I can't issue you a boarding pass. You're on the do-not-sail list.

MENELAUS
The do-not-sail list?

CASSANDRA AS PORT SECURITY OFFICER
You can either be on the list *or* on the ship—but not both.

MENELAUS
But I'm the king! Obviously, there's been some kind of mistake.

CASSANDRA AS PORT SECURITY OFFICER

Most likely. It's not a very accurate list. Poseidon himself was on the list for a while…. Nonetheless, a rule is a rule….

MENELAUS
I don't think you understand what's at stake here. My wife has been kidnapped….I *order* you to let me board that ship…

CASSANDRA AS PORT SECURITY OFFICER
I can't do that without proper authorization. Here at Pan-Hellenic Travel, security is our first priority….

MENELAUS
So how am I supposed to get this proper authorization?
CASSANDRA AS PORT SECURITY OFFICER
That's above my pay grade. You'll have to take that up with the gods.

3. **The Flagship of the Phylacean Fleet. King Protesilaus and Queen Laodamia.**
(Protesilaus enters. Laodamia follows. They have been arguing.)

PROTESILAUS
I don't see what you're all worked up about. You're the one who suggested taking a trip.

LAODAMIA
A trip, sure. But I meant the Riviera. Or sitting on the beach in Crete….Who ever heard of going on vacation to Troy?

PROTESILAUS
Don't say that so loud….As far as the world is concerned, this isn't a holiday. This is a business trip. Troy may not be as balmy as Crete, but it *is* tax deductible.

LAODOMIA
You and your tax deductions….What good are tax deductions when you're about to get slaughtered by Trojans….?

PROTESILAUS

(Protesilaus sits down on a chaise longue and begins reading the newspaper, possibly The Wall Street Journal.*)*
Tax deductions are like vacations. Once you've enjoyed a good one, nobody can ever take it away from you....

LAODAMIA

I don't see how you can remain so calm. If I were that calm, it would make me uneasy.... I'd think something was wrong with my nervous system. I'd die of a stroke worrying about being that a calm.

PROTESILAUS

What's the worst thing that could possibly happen?

LAODAMIA

The worst thing that could possible happen? Hold on a minute. I've composed a list.
(Laodamia removes the list from her pocket and reads; she slowly works herself into a frenzy.)
We could have left the gas range on while we were gone, and the children could asphyxiate in their sleep, or we could have left a pack of matches on the kitchen table, and the children could set the house on fire, or they could set the babysitter on fire, or the baby sitter could be a carrier of typhoid, or yellow fever, or Lyme disease, or the children could resent us for leaving them alone with the babysitter, and they could grow up psychologically damaged—like the apples at the supermarket that have those ugly welts on one side, or we could encounter a band of marauding pirates who make us walk the plank, who make us walk the plank naked, who laugh at us while we walk the plank naked, or the Trojans could grind us into chopped meat and serve us in fast food restaurants, or they could tie us up and tickle the soles of our feet until we reveal the secret access codes to the nuclear-equipped intercontinental ballistic missile launchers, or they could send us back to junior high school....Oh, God! I could have to be an ugly little Greek girl in a junior high school full of Trojans. Popular Trojans who make fun of me because once in

biology class I read aloud "orgasm" instead or "organism" by mistake....And after that, they'll follow me around moaning and calling me "Orgasm Girl." You can't imagine what it's like being called "Orgasm Girl" all through high school when you've never even had one!

(Pausing to compose herself; dignified.)

I suppose *that's* the worst thing that could happen.

PROTESILAUS

See. That's not really so bad, is it?

LAODAMIA

I hate it when you downplay my anxiety.

PROTESILAUS

I'm not downplaying your anxiety. I'm trying to comfort you.

(Looking up from his newspaper)

And Lyme disease isn't carried by people. It's carried by ticks....

LAODAMIA

Anxiety is important. It's an evolutionary advantage. Without anxiety, people would go around poking grizzly bears and tickling lions....Oh please, dearest. It's still not too late to turn back.

(Suddenly seductive)

If we go to Crete, I'll make it worth your while.

PROTESILAUS

(Sitting up, turning serious)

Look, honey. This trip is extremely important to me. If I tell you something, please promise me you won't worry....

LAODAMIA

If I did that, I'd worry about breaking my promise.....

PROTESILAUS

When we get to Troy, I'm going to be the first one off the ship.

LAODAMIA

Have you lost your mind?

PROTESILAUS
I've never felt so sane in my entire life.

LAODAMIA
But you heard the oracle. The first Greek to step foot on the shores of Troy is doomed to die on the battlefield.

PROTESILAUS
Don't believe everything you hear from the oracle......I'm quite determined.

LAODAMIA
What's gotten into you?

PROTESILAUS
You want to know the truth, honey? I have a list too. A list of worries. Just like yours.

LAODAMIA
You do?

PROTESILAUS
I do.
(Protesilaus removes the list from his pocket, clears his throat as though preparing to deliver a long speech, and reads.)
I'm afraid I'll die and be forgotten.
(A long pause.)

LAODAMIA
That's it?

PROTESILAUS
The first warrior to land on the beach at Troy will be remembered forever. The name Protesilaus will rank alongside Odysseus and Agamemnon in the annals of history. In three thousand years, school children will recite my name with awe and wonder.

LAODAMIA
But you'll be dead.

PROTESILAUS
In three thousand years? Of course, I'll be dead.

LAODAMIA
You'll be dead sooner. *I'll be alive* and you'll be dead.

PROTESILAUS
I'll be immortal.

LAODAMIA
Please don't do this. I'm begging you.

PROTESILAUS
Everything is going to be fine, honey. In any case, I'm confident that the oracle doesn't know what he's talking about. He's not a doctor, you know. You don't need a license to become an oracle....

LAODAMIA
Are you sure it's going to be okay?

PROTESILAUS
I'm positive.

LAODAMIA
Will you keep telling me it's going to be okay? Over and over again? Ten thousand times?

PROTESILAUS
Of course, it's going to be okay. You know what? I bet those Trojans will surrender without a fight.

4. Oenone and Helen.
(Oenone enters the hilltop where Helen is still bound. Oenone is sipping from a wine glass, or possibly a wine bottle, and appears conspicuously tipsy. The two women examine each other warily. After a pause, Oenone speaks.)

OENONE
Let me guess. You've been kidnapped by bandits.

HELEN

Actually, I—

OENONE

No, don't tell me....It wouldn't be bandits, would it? They'd
have taken your clothes.... I've got it. You're to be a human
sacrifice, and the high priest went to find firewood....

HELEN

If you'll please just—

OENONE

That's very noble of you, if you don't mind my saying so. Stupid, but noble. Not many pretty young girls are willing to be
burned on an altar these days....

HELEN

Please. You've got to help me.

OENONE

In my day, lots of girls volunteered to be sacrificed. It was either that—or marriage....

HELEN

What do you mean "in your day"? How old are you?

OENONE

Twenty-eight. The end of the line.

HELEN

Twenty-eight isn't *that* old.

OENONE

It's one hundred ninety-six in dog years.

HELEN

(Calculating)

Seven dog years for each human year....times twenty-eight....
carry the one....I suppose it *is* one hundred ninety-six in dog
years.

OENONE

Now it seems old, doesn't it?

HELEN
(Suddenly desperate)
You've got to help me. I'm not being sacrificed—I've been kid-
napped by a madman.

OENONE
I guessed bandits. That was close.

HELEN
Quick. He might come back at any moment. Could you please
untie me?

OENONE
I could….but I won't.

HELEN
You won't?!

OENONE
You *say* you've been kidnapped by a madman. But that's not
proof. Maybe *you're* the lunatic and you've been tied up for
your own protection….Or you're a slave being punished… Or
you and your partner are into some kinky fetish—I wouldn't
want to spoil all the fun….

HELEN
It's not like that. I'm Helen, Queen of Sparta.

OENONE
Yeah, sure. And I'm Athena, Goddess of Wisdom.

HELEN
(Sobbing)
I'm begging you. Show some compassion….as a woman….

OENONE
I really wish that I could help you. But there are liability issues
to think of….my legal duty to third parties….You might be
tied up out here for a very good reason. In any case, I'm confident this will all straighten itself out on its own….one way
or another….In the meantime, would you like a sip of wine?

HELEN
What type is it?

OENONE
Chablis.

HELEN
I drink only Zinfandel.

OENONE
Suit yourself.
(Oenone takes a swig and starts to leave.)

HELEN
Wait!

OENONE
I knew you'd reconsider. When you get right down to it, wine is wine....

HELEN
Can you at least tell someone that I'm out here? That the prince has gone mad and taken me captive?

THE EXECUTIONER

DANIELLE BARROS

Log line: In the 1950s, a Virginia death house executioner, an illiterate young man with a severe stutter, finds true friendship in a charismatic death house inmate. Through their unlikely friendship, within the prison walls, they find freedom.

FADE IN:

INT. PORTER'S CABIN - DAY - 1959

The one-room cabin is old, borderline dilapidated.

Daylight seeps in from the cracks between the wood. Sunlight

shines through a small, dingy window, bringing the dust in the room to life.

The bed is made, with old shoes lined up perfectly at the

foot. A black Officer's jacket hangs from a nail, topped with a black Officer's hat.

The room gives the impression that whoever lives there likes things in order.

PORTER, a man in his mid-twenties, dressed in worn jeans and a white tee-shirt, stands in front of an old record player.

His dark hair is tousled, his blue eyes intense as he carefully places the needle on the record, then walks over and sits down at a table in front of the window.

He is looking out the window, but his head blocks the view, making it so you can't see what he's looking at.

The STATIC, SCRATCHY sound of Johnny Cash's "CRY CRY CRY" begins to SOUND SOFTLY from the record player.

(POV) Porter's head turns down. On the worn-out table is a new sharpened pencil, piece of paper, half an untouched fried bologna sandwich, and a glass of water.

Porter reaches for the pencil, pauses, holding it somewhat awkwardly, then begins to write.

PORTER (V.O.)
(deep Southern drawl)
My name's Hank Porter, and like many of the men I've put to death, I too have killed for money. That'd be fifty-six people, to be exact. Paid for by the Commonwealth of Virginia.

(MORE)
I reckon that'd make me some sorta professional killer too. Though, that may be a thought best kept to myself. I can rightly say I ain't never killed nothin', not even a fly, without a court order. I reckon it makes me feel better knowing that. I often wonder how many men would still be breathin' if the judge or jury were the ones who had to pull that green lever; I'm guessin' quite a few. I've heard it mentioned by some that death at the hands of God is a natural, beautiful, transition of sorts...

FLASHBACK:

INT. PORTER'S FAMILY HOME LIVING ROOM - NIGHT

OVERHEAD SHOT

The living room looks like it had a woman's touch at one time, but has long since been neglected.

An empty vase and a dusty figurine collection sit on a table near a white sofa covered in a design of red roses.

A nine-year-old Porter sits on the floor, hugging his knees to his chest. Next to his feet his DAD lies, dressed in a

Prison Officer's uniform. He is FOAMING at the mouth, his eyes are wide open and fixed.

Porter looks up, you can see his face now. It is wet with tears, his eyes terrified, his mouth is open and twisted in anguish.

> PORTER (V.O.) (CONT'D)
> Havin' watched my daddy die, heart attack they say, it was an event that held no beauty that I can recall. Though, I saw it through the eyes of a boy; maybe as a grown man it would've been different... I reckon I'll never know.

EXT. FATHER'S FUNERAL - CEMETERY - MORNING

The cemetery is surrounded by green trees, lit by the warm morning sun.

2.

> PORTER (V.O.) (CONT'D)

A fairly large group of PEOPLE are attending a funeral.

The SOUND of BIRDS in the background begins to FADE as the SOUND of the PRIEST grows LOUDER.

A young Porter is standing in between WARDEN PARNELL and MRS. PARNELL. Porter is wearing pants that are too short, but his hair is combed neat and he is tidy.

Mrs. Parnell is a plain but attractive woman in her early 30s. She stands with her hand placed lovingly on Porter's shoulder.

Warden Parnell is a large, powerful man, in his early 40s.

His face is cold and emotionless, but his eyes are glossy with unshed tears. You know underneath his cold exterior, he cared deeply for Porter's father.

Behind them are twenty OFFICERS, all dressed in uniform, along with their WIVES and some WORKERS from the prison.

In the distance, MISS MAYBELLE, a large black woman, stands alone by a tree. She is dressed in black, and carries a white handkerchief in hand.

> PRIEST (O.S.)
> Let us commend our brother, Charles Porter, to the mercy of God. May his soul forever rest in peace with our Lord Savior, Jesus Christ, Amen. Ashes to ashes, dust to dust...

The Priest continues his blessing, his voice FADES, as the GRAVEDIG-GERS begin lowering the casket into the ground. It disappears into the earth.

A line of OFFICERS forms, beginning with Warden Parnell in front of the grave.

They each take turns shoveling in dirt, covering the casket.

You can see by the solemn looks on their faces that Charles

Porter was a well-respected man, and will be missed.

> PORTER (V.O.)
> My daddy worked as an officer in the Death House for nearly twenty years. And though he wasn't a big man, he walked tall, makin' him appear as such. Sometimes Warden Parnell'd say, "Son, your Daddy's as tough as nails, and twice as sharp." I always liked it when he be sayin' things like that.

3.

> (MORE)
> Sometimes he'd say, "Porter, you're just about as dumb as a load of bricks." I can't say I cared for that too much, but Miss Sally said he's just mad 'cause God give him the personality of a dishrag, and to pay him no mind, so I don't.

The funeral is over, people are starting to disperse. Some of the officers and their wives begin talking to each other. You can see Warden Parnell walking away without even a glance at Porter or his wife.

He continues past the crowd, walking alone. Mrs. Parnell watches her husband leave.

Her attention turns to a group of LADIES TALKING, she bends down and whispers something to Porter, he nods in agreement, she then goes over to join the conversation.

SHOT on MRS. GARRISON as she walks through the crowd towards Porter. She's in her early 30s, pin-up girl attractive, her dress is fitted tight, showing off her curves.

Some officers sneak a peak at her as she passes; the wives notice, but Mrs. Garrison is oblivious.

She stops in front of Porter, bends down, and puts her hand on his cheek, her fingernails are painted a glossy blood red.

(POV) Porter looks up at her in awe, as if seeing an angel.

>   MRS. GARRISON
>   (soft and soothing, deep Southern drawl)
>   Hey, Sugar. I'm so sorry 'bout your daddy. He was a good man,
>   about as good as they come. You know, I got a boy 'bout your
>   age. How'd you like to come over sometime, maybe stay for
>   supper? What's your most favorite thing to have for supper,
>   and I'll make sure to make it for ya'.

Porter stares up at her, eyes wide. She looks somewhat puzzled while she waits for Porter to answer.

He opens his mouth, and quickly closes it. Opens it again, and starts to STUTTER unintelligibly. You can see the strain and concentration in Porter's eyes.

4.

>   PORTER (V.O.) (CONT'D)

More than anything, he wants to tell her fried bologna sandwiches are his favorite, but he closes his mouth, looking to the ground, defeated.

Mrs. Garrison stands up, taken aback some, then places her hand on his shoulder and looks around. She catches Mrs. Parnell's eyes.

Mrs. Parnell excuses herself from the conversation, hurries over. She moves behind Porter, pulling him close to her body protectively.

You can tell by the way she's looking at Mrs. Garrison, she doesn't like her one bit.

> MRS. PARNELL
> (sharply, with contempt)
> He don't be talkin' none, on account of his lazy tongue. It's best you let him be now.

Mrs. Garrison turns her eyes from Mrs. Parnell to Porter.

She seems hurt, but undeterred by the cold, dismissive attitude Mrs. Parnell is giving her.

> MRS. GARRISON
> Well, how 'bout I make it a surprise then? Somethin' really special.

Mrs. Garrison is smiling sweetly at Porter, trying to make light of his stutter.

You can see the compassion in her eyes. Porter smiles wide in return, obviously excited about going to her house for supper.

> MRS. PARNELL
> (cold, dismissive)
> No thank you, Mrs. Garrison. Good day.

Mrs. Parnell quickly nods. Turning with Porter, she walks away, leaving Mrs. Garrison standing there.

Porter looks over his shoulder, you can see he desperately wants to say something to her.

> PORTER (V.O.)
> I ain't never cursed God for makin' it so I don't talk right, or for Warden Parnell makin' me this prison's executioner.

5.

(MORE)

But I'd be a lyin' man if I said I don't be cursing them empty benches some.
(beat)
Yes sir, I'd be a lyin' man indeed...

INT. PRISON'S DEATH CHAMBER - DAY

A room lit by a bright hanging light. A wooden electric chair sits ominously near the back wall. A viewing window is directly across, and on the far wall a green lever.

A young black INMATE is strapped to the electric chair. He strains vigorously against the thick leather straps that bind his chest, wrist and ankles.

His eyes turn frantically to Porter. The realization he's going to die any minute seems to set in as his breathing becomes short and panicked. He starts to cry and whimper.

Porter walks over to a bucket and pulls out a dark sponge soaked with water. The sound of DRIPPING water ECHOES eerily.

Porter looks to the viewing window. Through his reflection, he can see the benches are empty.

          PORTER (V.O.) (CONT'D)
    I know when that time comes, if them benches be empty, their
    last words surely gonna die with me in that room, and their
    bodies'll most likely be laid to rest in a grave bearing only the
    numbers on their shirts...

EXT. PRISON'S GRAVEYARD - DAY

A neglected graveyard with hundreds of dingy white crosses bearing only carelessly etched numbers.

          PORTER (V.O.) (CONT'D)
    It just don't seem right burying people that way. Hell, I reckon
    even some dogs get buried with more care...
        (beat)
    No, it just don't seem right at all.

                                      CUT BACK:

PORTER (V.O.) (CONT'D)

Porter places the sponge on the inmate's brutally shaved head, water drips downs the inmate's face, mixing with his fallen tears.

Porter then places a leather cap, lined with copper, over the sponge, connects a clamp to the rod protruding from the cap, and then places a clamp on the inmate's leg.

The cold look on Porter's face and his calculated movements give the impression he's indifferent to the dying man.

> INMATE
> (voice shaking)
> Oh my God... Oh my God. Please... (straining his neck to look at Porter, but he can't see him)
>
> ...please tell my mama I'm sorry!
>
> Please tell her I ain't never meant nobody no harm, please! Oh my God, Mama.

Openly sobbing when he calls out for his mom.

> PORTER (V.O.)
> I ain't never known my mama, bein' she died on account of me bein' born. But sometimes when them inmates be crying for their mama, I feel like cryin' out for mine too.
>
> Miss Sally said sometimes love don't make no sense, and I reckon she's right.

> INMATE (CONT'D)
> Dear Lord, oh Jesus, please forgive me my sins.

Porter walks in front of the inmate, leans over and places his hand on his trembling shoulder, squeezing hard, while looking dead center into his wide eyes. He figures a man who's about to die deserves to be seen, so he sees him. Porter stands up and pulls over a black piece of cloth, connected to the leather cap, covering the inmate's face.

(POV) Porter walks across the room, glancing over to the empty viewing window as he passes. A look of anger crosses his face.

The SOUND of the inmate SINGING in a CHOKED, NERVOUS, WEAK voice emanates from behind him.

>   INMATE (O.C.)
>   (singing)
>   I FOUND MY THRILL... ON BLUEBERRY HILL... ON
>   BLUEBERRY HILL... WHEN I FOUND YOU... THE MOON
>   STOOD STILL... ON BLUEBERRY HILL...

Porter turns a dial, waits for a green light to appear. He then places his hand around the chipped green lever, looks up towards the heavens, then closes his eyes tight.

>   PORTER (V.O.)
>   I don't know if God be hearing them, since they be con-
>   demned men and all, so I say their name, and repeat their
>   words in my head as loud as I can, hopin' maybe that'll help.

                                                            CUT TO:

                                                          MONTAGE:

CLOSE-UP SHOTS on the faces of all the past inmates Porter has executed. Some look angry, some quiet in prayer, most crying. Shot ends on empty benches.

                                                  BACK TO SCENE:

Porter pulls the lever. The inmate's singing dies as the HUM of electricity ECHOES throughout the room.

He returns the lever upright, turns the dial, giving more juice, then pulls the lever down again, this time quickly returning it upright.

He looks to the inmate, whose head is now slumped over. He glances to the viewing window, still empty.

Porter walks over and begins to remove the binds and cap. By the way he's touching everything you can tell it's all still hot.

Porter puts the dark, steaming sponge back in the bucket of water. Picking up the bucket, he makes his way towards the door.

The WARDEN, DOCTOR, and three OFFICERS walk in, talking lively amongst each other. Just another day at work. An

OFFICER trails behind them, rolling in a large table.

Porter stands to the side and lets him pass. Only the Warden looks at Porter.

8.

MUSIC: FATS DOMINO, "BLUEBERRY HILL"

Porter starts to walk out the door, in the background you can see the doctor halfheartedly check for a pulse, then the officers pick up and roughly move the dead inmate to the table.

Porter stops and lets an elderly black JANITOR with a mop and bucket pass, then continues on.

As Porter walks down the corridor, you can see the inmate being rolled away in opposite direction.

> PORTER (V.O.)
> I carry their names in my heart, like a fishin' weight pullin'
> down from my chest. If it weren't for Bobby Walker teachin'
> me to write as he done, I reckon my heart'd most likely be
> too heavy for my chest by now. Miss Sally once told me that
> when lookin' into a man's eyes, she could see straight into
> his heart, and that mine was the finest heart she'd ever seen.
> I often wonder when Miss Sally be lookin' into my eyes now
> what kinda heart she be lookin' at... I reckon it ain't the finest
> she'd ever seen no more.

FLASHBACK:

EXT. DIRT ROAD - MORNING

A narrow dirt road cuts through the tall trees. Wild bluebells grow on either side. It's vibrant and full of life.

The SOUNDS of BIRDS and WOODPECKERS ECHO in the background.

13-year-old PORTER is walking with a stick, hitting pebbles along the way.

You can see an 11-year-old MISS SALLY in the distance walking up quickly behind Porter. She is a pretty girl, her hair is red and carelessly tied back in a ponytail.

> MISS SALLY
> Hey! You there!

Porter begins to quicken his steps. You can see by the look on his face he'd rather be walking alone.

9.

> MISS SALLY
> (frustrated)
> Hey! Wait up!

Porter can hear her footsteps closing in. With a long exhale he stops walking, but doesn't turn around.

> MISS SALLY
> What, are you deaf or somethin'?

Miss Sally moves to stand in front of Porter, she's smiling.

Porter looks down, and starts to move the stick around the dirt, shaking his head from side to side in answer.

> MISS SALLY
> I thought since we was goin' the same way, maybe we'd walk togetha', keepin' each other's company. My name's Sally Gallagher.

She extends her hand in confidence. Porter looks at her hand, then looks up at her, and reluctantly places his hand in hers. Her smile widens.

> MISS SALLY

Well? Ain't you got a name?

>PORTER
>(awkwardly, on tail end of a hot breath, stuttering)
>H-H-H-aaank.

Miss Sally slowly releases his hand. She looks at him a moment, then hooks her arm in his and starts walking, pulling him along.

Porter looks surprised, as if he expected her to walk off laughing at him.

>MISS SALLY
>(endless chatterbox)
>Hank. Well, that sure is a fine name. You know they say my Pa's the spittin' image of ole Hank Williams. Yes sir, they do. Though they also say my Pa' couldn't carry a tune if it was handed to him in a bucket. I reckon he does sound more like a howlin' dog than Mister Hank Williams. But that don't be stoppin' my Pa none, no sir...

BACK TO CAMERA SHOT as they continue down the road.

10.

Miss Sally's voice starts to FADE as the CAMERA slowly ZOOMS OUT.

>MISS SALLY (V.O.)
>He be singin' that song "Hey Good Looking" to my Ma most every night. You know that song? Well, God help her if she don't bust a gut laughin' nearly every time.

A series of DISSOLVE SHOTS plays, showing them growing older.

The last shot is of Porter and Miss Sally at around nineteen.

He is tall, with broad shoulders. Her hair is still pulled back into a careless ponytail, but her figure now shows the curves of womanhood.

She places her head on Porter's shoulder as they walk.

INT. PRISON DEATH HOUSE - DAY

Gray, rusty steel, DARK and IMPOSING. The place men come to die. Long row of two-tier cells facing a stone wall. Only a few small windows are visible from the second tier.

CAMERA TRACKS PORTER as he walks along the cell doors, pushing a SQUEAKY metal cart carrying trays of unappetizing food.

In the background, the ominous NOISE of CLANKING metal doors mixes with the mishmash of inmate CHATTER.

Porter moves down the row of cells, stopping in front of each cell, he hands in a supper tray to waiting black hands.

The SOUND of a MAN'S deep LAUGHTER cuts through the background noise, causing Porter to look up from his cart.

He sees BOBBY WALKER, a tall, slender, boyishly handsome man, standing with OFFICER SHARP, OFFICER COOLEY, and OFFICER RED at his back, and with OFFICER KENTUCKY JIM at his front.

Bobby is grinning wide while looking at Officer Kentucky Jim.

Porter can't hear what they're saying, but by Kentucky Jim's reddened neck and balled up fist, he can tell he's not too happy about it.

Porter moves faster down the line, his curiosity uncharacteristically getting the better of him.

>   PORTER (V.O.)
> I remember the first time I laid eyes on Bobby Walker.

11.

>   (MORE)
> With seeing mostly Negroes in the Death House, he looked about as white as a bed sheet, with hair as black as the bird known for that color. It was that smile, though, spread wide 'cross his face, that looked the most peculiar. I ain't never seen nobody brought into this Death House looking so plumb tickled to be there.

Porter moves in close enough to hear what they're saying.

OFF. KENTUCKY JIM
What'd you say to me, boy?

BOBBY WALKER
(sarcastically calm)
Why, I have no idea what you're referring to, Capt'n.

OFF. CHARLIE MONROE
(eager to see a fight)
He said your mama...

OFF. KENTUCKY JIM
(eyes glaring)
Can it, Charlie! I know exactly what this little piece of shit said!

The inmate background CHATTER starts to quiet some. A couple of inmates take this opportunity to call out crude comments anonymously to the officers.

Off. Charlie Monroe, pissed off at being put in his place, mumbles under his breath while backing up a few steps.

Off. Red, clearly the oldest among them, walks off. BOBBY continues to smile coyly.

Off. Kentucky Jim, a short and muscular man, walks up close enough to BOBBY that their chests are almost touching.

Because of the height difference, Off. Kentucky Jim has to look up at Bobby, you can see that pisses him off.

OFF. KENTUCKY JIM
(face red, spitting words)
Take a good look at my face, boy, 'cause it's gonna be the last thing you see before I pull that lever on Old Sparky, cookin' you up like a stuffed pig.

12.

PORTER (V.O.) (CONT'D)

(MORE)
I can guarantee you ain't gonna be smilin' then, boy, but I
surely will.

Bobby's smile slowly fades. Off. Kentucky Jim takes a step back, clearly
pleased with himself for his assumed intimidation of Bobby.

OFF. KENTUCKY JIM
(amused)
Get him outta here, before he pisses himself.

He starts motioning for the other officers to take Bobby to his cell.

His hand stops, suspended in air, when Booby starts to speak.

BOBBY WALKER
I know I will die here, and maybe even by your hand. But I
can guarantee you this...

BOBBY places his hand over his heart, dramatically.

BOBBY WALKER
The love I have for your dear mama I will carry in my heart
from this life to the next.

The other Officers start clearing their throats in an attempt to hide their
laughter. LAUGHTER erupts from the cells.

Porter stops walking when he hears what Bobby said. He looks up, fear
and astonishment mark his eyes.

Bobby smiles crooked, clearly amused by the enraged look on Off. Kentucky Jim's face.

OFF. KENTUCKY JIM
You son of a bitch!

As if on cue, the other officers grab Bobby, holding back his arms, while
Off. Kentucky Jim releases his fury upon him.

The brutal force of his punches ECHOES throughout the cell block.

Off. Kentucky Jim grows tired, and motions for Off. Sharp and Off. Cooley to drag Bobby to his cell.

>   OFF. KENTUCKY JIM
>   (out of breath)
>   Get him outta here.

>   OFF. KENTUCKY JIM (CONT'D)

He spits on Bobby before walking away.

They drag Bobby's seemingly lifeless body in front of Porter, who stands at the cell door, holding a supper tray. Porter stays outside the cell, listening.

LAUGHTER SOUNDS from in the cell. Porter straightens up as he hears their voices getting closer. Off. Sharp stops in front of Porter, staring him down. Porter holds his ground.

>   OFF. SHARP
>   If he does up n' die, we'll just say Porter here did it. He ain't
>   gonna say no different. Are you, boy?

Off. Sharp gives up on intimidating Porter. Both Officers walk off, LAUGHING. Porter watches them leave, then walks into Bobby's cell, carrying the supper tray.

He finds Bobby curled up on the bloodied floor. He sets down the supper tray and turns to leave. He hesitates at the cell door. He sticks his head out, looks from side to side, and then turns, quickly walking back into the cell.

He bends down, moving his arms under Bobby's limp body.

Porter struggles with Bobby's weight as he brings him over to the cot.

(POV) Bobby cracks open his eyes, looks to Porter in a daze.

>   BOBBY WALKER
>   (soft, dazed)
>   My mama said my mouth was gonna be my ruination.

Smiles, showing bloody teeth. Then closes his eyes.

BOBBY WALKER

I reckon she's right. I figure they can break this body, but my spirit will remain whole. Yes sir, when that time comes it's gonna soar.

Porter gets him situated on the cot. Bobby MOANS at the movement. Porter stands up, looking down at him in question.

OFF. RED (O.S.)

Unless you plan on kissin' him goodnight, I'd suggest you get goin' now, Porter.

Porter jumps, startled by the sudden voice, and turns around. You can see he relaxes when he sees who it is.

14.

Off. Red walks in, carrying an old army medic bag.

He is in his early 50s, and is tall and thin. His hair is mostly gray, with strands of red betraying its youthful color.

He walks to the edge of the cot, sets down the medic bag, begins to examine Bobby. Bobby begins to GROAN at his prodding. Porter walks over to the cell door but doesn't leave.

OFF. RED

(firm, fatherly)

I have a good mind to sew that mouth of yours shut, boy. You know what tonight is? It's meatloaf night, and 'cause of your big mouth it's gonna be cold and dry by the time I get home. Not to mention the earful I'm gonna to get from the missus.

Off. Red pries open Bobby's eyes, shining in a light.

BOBBY WALKER

(voice strained with pain)

Sorry, Doc.

OFF. RED

I ain't no Doc, and you ain't sorry. What's your name, boy?

                    BOBBY WALKER
          Bobby Walker.

                    OFF. RED
          And how old are you, Bobby Walker?

                    BOBBY WALKER
          Twenty-two.

Off. Red finishes with his examination and starts putting away his equipment.

                    OFF. RED
          Well, Bobby Walker, of twenty-two years, looks like you will
          live to see anotha' day. In most cases I would say that's good
          news. Though, in your case I wouldn't.

                    BOBBY WALKER
                    (laughing, grimacing in pain with the motion)
          I reckon you're right 'bout that.

                                                                    15.

With a nod of his head, Off. Red picks up his bag and starts to leave, shaking his head at Porter as he walks past.

Porter follows, locking the cell door behind him. He turns around, pushing his cart, picking up empty trays as he passes.

He glances back to Bobby's cell, then keeps walking, collecting trays with a small smile.

                    PORTER (V.O.)
          I'd gathered two things upon first meetin' Bobby Walker. We
          was about the same age, and he was certified crazy for sure.
          I'd heard my daddy say once, you get more respect as a cra-
          zy man than a stupid one. I reckon he was right about that.
          Though, lookin' at Bobby Walker then, it sure seemed crazy
          hurt a hell of a lot more. After that day, I bet old Red wished
          he woulda sewn that mouth of Bobby's shut, bein' he got a
          beat-down nearly every day thereafter. *

GRAND PRIZE

A Marriage of Inconvenience
Jacob M. Appel, New York NY

CHILDREN'S/YOUNG ADULT FICTION WINNERS

1. *A Unicorn's Horn Tastes Like Vanilla*
   Brooke Hartman, Chugiak AK

2. *Dead Girl Finds Home*
   Heather Sappenfield, Vail CO

3. *And the Elephants Came*
   Kim Tomsic, Boulder CO

4. *The Secret Life of Sleeping Beauty*
   Charity Tahmaseb, Minnetonka MN

5. *Lucky Strike*
   Athena Franco, Great Lakes IL

6. *Epic High*
   Yael Tischler, Vancouver, BC, Canada

7. *Leprechaun Tours Australia*
   Rick Keuning, Leichhardt, Australia

8. *Why I'm In Detention*
   Adeaze Simmons, Stanton CA

9. *Chef Harry Dickens*
   Claude Gauthier, Winnipeg MB, Canada

10. *Black Water*
    Barb Miller, Wenatchee WA

GENRE SHORT STORY WINNERS

1. *Making Good Neighbors*
   Ann M. Sligar, Carthage MO

2. *Baneberry Fire*
   Conner Jefferson Bennie Jones II,
   Murrieta CA

3. *Cereal Killer*
   John Brizzi, Shreveport LA

4. *In The Beginning*
   William Dunkerley, Waverly NY

5. *Betrayal*
   Melanie Stringham, Alamogordo NM

6. *The Body*
   Karen Rought, Greene NY

7. *Water's Breadth Apart*
   Bryan Alexander, Mesquite TX

8. *Jello*
   Laura L. Farnsworth, Denver CO

9. *Year Of The Bright Star, On The Day Of Salt*
   Annette Kohlmeister (Anne Kohl),
   Colorado Springs CO

10. *Catching Sparks*
    Irene Hsu, San Jose CA

INSPIRATIONAL WRITING WINNERS

1. *The Song of the Saw-whet Owl*
   Edward A. Hara, Fairfax VA

2. *There Are Three of Us*
   A.E. Wasserman, Burbank CA

3. *The Woman in Red*
   Diane Tarantini, Morgantown WV

4. *Sacrifice of the Zwasos*
   Sherri Gragg, Franklin TN

5. *The Gift*
   Marielena Zuniga, Langhorne PA

6. *Welcome to Paradise*
   Joanne Cameron, Jupiter FL

7. *Rain*
   Janis H. Coverdale, Windsor CA

8. *A Lesson In Grace*
   Courtney Grier Williams, Valparaiso IN

9. *Evolutions of Exodus*
   Michael Lee, Lawrence KS

10. *Light in the Dark*
    Deirdre Assenza, Mt. Lebanon PA

MAGAZINE FEATURE ARTICLE WINNERS

1. *Greek Goddess of Kitchen and Block"*
   Elaine K. Howley, Waltham MA

2. *There's a Cat in our House!*
   David B. Whitlock, Lebanon KY

3. *From Lawn to Wildflower Meadow*
   Garrett A. Hughes, Honeoye Falls NY

4. *A Perfect trip*
   Sandrine Marlier, New York NY

5. *Matt Savage: A Cracker Jack Jazz Pianist*
   Lisa Cahn, Huntington NY

6. *The Veteran, Thank-You!*
   Klex Carmichael, Clinton MA

7. *Remembering the Fallen*
   Mark Ray, Louisville KY

8. *The Escape Artist*
   Paul Fein, Agawam MA

9. *Getting Kids to Love Reading*
   Marina DelVecchio, Cary NC

10. *Letting Go of Fear*
    Jennifer Bridgman, Mountain View CA

MAINSTREAM/LITERARY SHORT STORY WINNERS

11. *Silent Movies/Short Story*
    Yoon-Ji Han, Tai Tam, Hong Kong

12. *The Photo Under the Pantyhose*
    Bonnie Engstrom, Scottsdale AZ

13. *Loop*
    Meghan Barrett Cousino, Chicago IL

14. *Mandela's Soldier*
    Ann Robson, Oceanside CA

15. *Thicker Than Blood*
    Ilene Goldman, Lake in the Hills IL

16. *Sold!*
    Mary Nugent, Bushkill PA

17. *Daddy's Pride and Joy*
    Sheryl L. Ricigliano, Golden CO

18. *One Little Rabbit*
    Tom Juergens, Hamilton MA

19. *Second Chances*
    Robert G. Rentz, Fort Myer FL

20. *A Snag of Hope*
    Jeff Mathison, Spring Mills PA

MEMOIR/PERSONAL ESSAY WINNERS

1. *Natural Science*
   Randy Osborne, Atlanta GA

2. *Saucer Eyes*
   Joseph Walls, Doylestown PA

3. *If Tomorrow Never Comes...*
   Jocelyn Cerrudo Sese, Queens Village NY

4. *What Lies Beneath*
   Gypsy Martin, Camas WA

5. *Can I Stay?*
   Donna Emmary, Winston-Salem NC

6. *The Dancing Skeletons*
   Melissa Ambrosino, Hattiesburg MS

7. *The Magic Tumor Theory*
   Sondra Raines Brooks, Spicewood TX

8. *Surviving Myself in Spite of Myself*
   Derek Mohn, Plymouth MA

9. *The Cheetah*
   Teri Byrd, Volcano HI

10. *Car Keys for Children*
    Sarajoy Van Boven, Spokane WA

NON-RYMING POETRY WINNERS

1. *Ethereal Existence*
   Claire Elizabeth Scherzinger, Toronto ON, Canada

2. *Burning the Bodies*
   Dawn Manning, Lansdowne PA

3. *A Rented Yard on a Gulf Coast Morning*
   Nikki Pencak, Monroeville PA

4. *This Crucifix of Need*
   Suzanne Burns, Bend OR

5. *Snow Falling on Venus*
   Marla Alupoaicei, Frisco TX

6. *In the Quiet*
   Gladys L. Henderson, Nesconset NY

7. *Eating at The Museum of Fine Arts*
   Suellen Wedmore, Rockport MA

8. *Up From The Chinese Cabbage*
   George Handy, Asheville NC

9. *A Beloved Introduction*
   Martha Hanneman Whitfield, Dearborn MI

10. *When I Haven't Been Kissed*
    Suellen Wedmore, Rockport MA

RHYMING POETRY WINNERS

1. *Painted Postcard from Japan*
   Michelle Perez, Secaucus NJ

2. *My Cousin's Son Remounces His Nativity*
   Melissa Canno, Nashville TN

3. *As One Delighted*
   Mary Flynn, Apopka FL

4. *Himalayas*
   Diana H. Kolaczkowska, Palo Alto CA

5. *Come!*
   Michael R. Burch, Nashville TN

6. *Ode to Dame Agatha*
   Suellen Wedmore, Rockport MA

7. *Break Then*
   Susanna Grady, Plymouth MA

8. *Depression, Explained*
   Vicki L. Weavil, Winston-Salem NC

9. *The Thanksgiving*
   Jessica Wierzbinski, Salida CO

10. *Canis Domesticus (aka "An Ode to Dagmar")*
    Katy Regnery, Ridgefield CT

STAGE PLAY WINNERS

1. *Helen of Sparta*
   Jacob M. Appel, New York NY

2. *In The Floodplain*
   Jacob M. Appel, New York NY

3. *Arborophilia*
   Jacob M. Appel, New York NY

4. *Confessionall*
   Anthony Hall Seed, Frankfort IL

5. *The Book of Lost Fathers*
   Steve Purcell, Philadelphia PA

6. *3 ½ Minutes*
   Laura Zlatos, Brooklyn NY

7. *Elephants and Other Worldly Dilemmas*
   Dina Laura, Astoria NY

8. *Acting Funny*
   M J Daspit, Ashland OR

9. *Purgatory*
   Ben Steele, Kitchener ON

10. *The Kindness of Strangers*
    Jacob M. Appel, New York NY

TELEVISION/MOVIE SCRIPT WINNERS

1. *The Executioner*
   Danielle Barros, Belmont CA

2. *Gray Matter*
   Michael Balin, Long Beach CA

3. *Gone South*
   Erik R. Slagle, Linden NJ

4. *Sun City*
   Matthew Minson, Spring TX

5. *Blistered Moon*
   Jeff Ingram, Newport OR

6. *Looking for Lila Ray*
   Linda Niccol, Kapiti, New Zealand

7. *Barkers Upon Tyne-Pilot*
   Garry Berman and Kelly Thompson,
   Westhampton NJ

8. *Shoot For The Stars*
   Janson Mancheski, Green Bay WI

9. *Garbo's Last Stand*
   Jon James Miller, Oakland CA

10. *Stealing Shakespeare*
    Jason Ford, Portland OR